BEDOUINS

BEDOUINS
THE SINAI NOMADS

Photography: Shlomo Arad
Text: Sami Michael

Massada

To my wife, Geulie,

"I remember thee, the kindness of
thy youth,...
When thou wentest after me in the
wilderness,
In a land that was not sown."

Jeremiah 2:2

Foreword

I did not come to the Sinai as a photographer in search of an exotic subject to be documented and immortalized. This book is almost an incidental result of a very personal relationship which evolved over a period of many years, at a slow desert-like (Bedouin) pace, between the writer of these lines and the people and landscape of the desert.

Many artists – in various disciplines from music to painting and sculpture – have been inspired by the Sinai landscape. The "virgin landscape" is a superlative frequently used in describing their Sinai experience. I am not a landscape photographer, and for me the landscape served only as background – and not only as a photographer – to understand the people; for it is the desert landscape – the topography, the climate, the vegetation – that largely determines the Bedouin way of life.

I spent long stretches of time in the Sinai over a period of more than ten years. Yet, I do not pretend to know the desert or its people. The Bedouins live in a closed, traditional society, which by virtue of being such has succeeded in surviving in extremely difficult climatic, economic and political conditions.

At the beginning of my way in Sinai, I was among the many others who made the mistake of interpreting the Bedouin tradition of hospitality as a sign of openness inviting intimacy. It took me some time before I realized that the tradition of hospitality, like many other Bedouin customs, is the product of the harsh realities of life in an arid and desolate region.

The better the Bedouins and I came to know one another, the more they expected of me, in terms of my mode of behavior. You can not act like a guest and become intimate. If you wish to become 'one of the family' – you had to undergo a process of 're-education'.

Photographing the Bedouins required great patience and affection for the 'subjects'. It required a reorientation on such concepts as time, freedom, privacy, loyalty, and honor. It took years of good will to understand, and to accept that which it is not possible (for us as strangers) to understand in the life style of the man of the desert. Long months passed before I felt comfortable enough with the Bedouins to take out my camera. My photographs gave them pleasure and decorated their tents and their camels. It was all done with great care and hesitation, fearing to penetrate forbidden domains, to invade privacy or violate trust – where the line separating what is permitted and what is forbidden was so thin and precarious.

I wasn't thinking of a book. I began photographing the Bedouins because that was the only thing I could do to give them pleasure (apart from helping to dig wells). At a later stage, I had another motive. I feared that the extensive encounter with 'progress' and technology might lead to the annihilation of traditional Bedouin society and I wished to capture it on film. But I was wrong. Years passed before I came to understand the inner vitality of Bedouin society, its ability to absorb outside influence for the purpose of improving its life without allowing that influence to undermine its nature. As the basket-weaver from A Tur once said to me, "there were the Turks, the British, the Egyptians, and now the Israelis. They all come and go, and only we remain true to the desert. Who, then, is the strongest among us?"

And, indeed, many of us who spent long periods of time in Sinai came to understand the power of tradition and the significance of loyalty for the man of the desert. The Bedouin is loyal only to his family and to his tribe, which serves as the source of his strength and his status. Although I developed close relations with the Bedouins, I never really thought of them as close friends. Only a Bedouin — someone who shares his fate — can be a friend to a Bedouin.

As the time of the Israeli evacuation of Sinai drew near, I used to make frequent trips to the Sinai, bringing a variety of supplies for my Bedouin friends, who were afraid (and justly so) that the seven good years were drawing to an end. On the eve of the evacuation the Gebeliya Tribe, in the region of Saint Catherine's Monastery, threw a farewell party. Although the separation was a very sad one for me, it was less so for them. They were used to changes and changing rulers.

After a short time, when Sinai was already under Egyptian rule, I returned to Saint Catherine's to cover the visit of President Sadat, who had come to pray at the foot of Mount Sinai. All the Bedouins of the region, dressed in their finery, gathered 'joyfully' to greet their new ruler. The king is dead — long live the new king. Not one of my former friends — and there were many present who knew me and had considered me a friend — came to say hello or to invite me to tea or to spend the night. The very fact that this did not surprise me was proof that I knew the Bedouins well, even if I did not understand them completely.

A few words are in order regarding photographing in Sinai and the photographs in this book. The cruel light of the desert allows only a few hours suited for taking pictures. Only a few hours in the morning and two or three hours before sunset are suitable for gaining the proper color quality. Needless to say, not all the photographs were taken during such optimum hours.

I knew all my 'subjects' personally, some better than others. My being acquainted with them sometimes created limitations, which may have curtailed the output of photographs; however, I don't pretend that this book is an exhaustive study of the Bedouins, and I hope, instead, that it will serve as an expression of my esteem for them as people and for their way of life.

Shlomo Arad

Introduction

No geographic area can be described without reference to its inhabitants and no human community can be understood without reference to the geographic area in which it lives.

It may seem that this assumption does not apply to nomadic tribes, whose way of life is based on wandering from one place to another. The Bedouin appears to have no emotional attachment to the particular plot of land on which he happens to have pitched his tent. When he departs he leaves nothing behind. Ho doesn't strike root in any one place, and there seems to be no reciprocal relationship between himself and the land. On the face of it, he behaves like a guest in his own homeland. He is emotionally ever ready to pull up his tent, to gather his scant belongings, take his livestock and move on to more promising horizons.

A figure such as this must ever puzzle the imagination of the city dweller or the villager, who has struck root in one place. A permanent settler amasses material possessions and forms an emotional attachment to the place where he lives; he feels that his world would crumble if something disrupted the reciprocity of his relationship with the home he lives in or his place of work – the office or factory where he spends many hours, or the fields he cultivates. He establishes a solid network of friendships and family ties which make him feel secure. He tends his cemeteries and other remains of the past in order to emphasize continuity. He looks upon himself as a dot revolving in bounding circles on a piece of land whose horizon is constant and unchanging. He remains in place while the years pass him by; he awaits the coming of summer, the dying of autumn, the storms of winter and the splendor of spring. He digs in and allows the seasons to pass like a person sitting on a veranda and watching a colorful parade go by.

Obviously, the permanent settler would find it difficult to understand the Bedouin who, like a turtle, carries his home on his back and pursues the seasons of the year. The permanent settler, who for thousands of years has been inventing and perfecting countless means of contriving to maintain his way of life despite the changing of the seasons, will find it strange that the Bedouins seem to live their life precisely by the changing seasons.

Feelings towards the Bedouins such as curiosity, suspicion, misunderstanding, admiration, contempt and hatred characterize not only the modern-day city dweller, who has made the city shaped by modern technology the focus of his life, but also the villager and town dweller of older times. Such feelings have produced several contradictory attitudes towards the Bedouins, which have become firmly established among permanent settlers and have been passed on from one generation to the next.

One such attitude is the romantic approach, which views the Bedouin as a person pure and free as the wind. Galloping on his camel, he subdues the horizon. He is born free, loves the wide-open spaces and will accept no bonds or restrictions. The Bedouin is a proud, self-confident being who will yield to no man or rival. He is clean and healthy, and leads a well-balanced, well-adjusted life. His speech is pure, clear and full of wisdom. Hundreds of years ago, teachers of Arabic who were fanatic purists of the language used to tell their pupils: "Those who wish to learn true and pure Arabic must go and live among the Bedouins for one year." Thus the romantic approach to the Bedouins is not exclusively limited to Europeans such as Lawrence of Arabia and other Westerners. It is also prevalent among Arabs.

There is a mystic approach to the Bedouins, one which binds together the power of prophecy, the desert and the Bedouins. Most prophets did, after all, have their revelations in the desert, or found sanctuary there after fleeing from their pursuers. The burning bush which Moses saw was a desert bush, and it was in the desert that he heard the voice of God. The Torah was given to Moses on a typical desert mountain. It was in the desert open spaces surrounding Mecca, rather than in his home in the holy city itself, that God revealed himself to Mohammed.

This approach views the Bedouins as mystical beings who know much and say little, wandering in wide-open spaces and constantly undergoing a process of creation, in a landscape of shifting sands whose contours change with the changing winds.

He is a silent philosopher, and when he speaks his words are pearls of wisdom. He finds his way in a roadless landscape, as if attuned to voices which no human ear but his can hear. He is in touch with the winds and the stars. He can concoct effective cures for impotence, infertility, madness, cancer, fever, diarrhea, bad luck, and indifference to a lover's sighs. He is endowed with supernatural powers. He can bestow blessings on the needy with his power for good or kill with the power of the evil eye.

There is also a defensive approach to the Bedouins, one which is mainly apologetic. The Bedouin is not like a locust leaving behind him destruction and desolation, but rather like a creature that lives in wondrous harmony with the delicate biological balance in a harsh and cruel environment. This naive approach is prevalent among intellectuals of Bedouin descent and is a response to the view which holds that the Bedouin is a "creator of deserts," that is, he destroys the vegetation and animal life in his environment to satisfy his immediate needs, leaving behind him a devastated wasteland. These intellectuals maintain that the desert existed before the Bedouin, but he alone had the courage to penetrate it. He loved it, remained in it as a loyal partner. He alone was able to adapt himself to its conditions, and to abide by its laws. In that wondrous ecological system which evolved in the desert, he found a niche for himself. He was able to play a role in the balance of that system, using his intelligence to gain an advantage over the other desert creatures, to use them for his benefit and to establish a benign dominion over them. The desert and its creatures willingly accepted this friendship.

An approach which resorts to such oversimplification calls to mind the mystical attitude which endows the Bedouins with the qualities of the researcher rather than those of the object of research. The following story serves as a good example:

An army unit encamped in the desert near where a Bedouin had pitched his tent with his family and flocks.

After a while, close ties were established between the soldiers and the Bedouin, who quickly adjusted to the leftovers of the soldiers' field rations. The Bedouin felt that he must somehow show his gratitude to the soldiers and soon he established himself as their weather forecaster. Every evening the soldiers would gather round him and ask what weather to expect in the coming days. The Bedouin would fix them with a penetrating look, remain silent for a long time as if listening to voices from another world, and then announce the weather forecast. His forecasts were never wrong. They were as accurate as if he had been equipped with his own sophisticated meteorological station, aided by satellite photographs. Even the skeptics among the soldiers stopped mocking him and were forced to admit they had been wrong. The mystics felt their victory keenly. The Bedouin became an institution. However, one of the soldiers, who was a very curious fellow and an investigator at heart, refused to accept the matter at face value and was determined to discover the cause behind the effect. He became close friends with the Bedouin and would talk to him for hours, trying to discover the secret of his prophetic power. The Bedouin became very fond of this soldier and once, when he was again asked by the soldier to reveal his secret, he finally relented. He gave the soldier the look of an amused child, entered the tent, and withdrew from beneath his mattress a small box enclosed in a black plastic case.

"Why, that's a transistor radio!" exclaimed the soldier.

"That's right," said the Bedouin and proudly added, "Every day I listen to the news. I also hear the weather report."

When simple facts are ignored or forgotten, explanations become simplistic and naive. The claim that "the Bedouin was brave enough to enter the desert, loved it, and remained as its friend" presupposes that there are whole human communities which, as a matter of choice, prefer a hard life in a harsh environment. And to claim that the desert and its creatures happily accepted the Bedouin's friendship is to endow a piece of land and the creatures which live on it with human qualities. Even if we assume that barren mountains, flocks of birds, coral colonies and solitary trees are capable of emotion, it is a bit far fetched to suppose that a tree that has been chopped down is ecstatic about being fed to a bonfire, or that a bird will sing for joy while being shot down to enrich a Bedouin's meal of rice.

Then there is the view firmly held by the inhabitants of permanent settlements which border on the desert, whereby the Bedouins are far from the heartwarming figures portrayed by foreign romantics and by the few intellectuals of Bedouin descent who are now cut off from their origins and who look back wistfully on their past. Neither is he anything like the figure depicted in early Arabic poetry. This view of the Bedouin is not at all flattering. He is seen as a thief, a sly, contemptible creature, ignorant, filthy, diseased and starving, freezing in the cold and enfeebled by the heat. 'Like a Bedouin' is a common expression in permanent Arab settlements, and the epithet is definitely intended to be derogatory. Here, when someone is said to be 'like a Bedouin', he is certainly not being likened to the legendary image held by the romantics and mystics, associated with grandeur and arousing admiration. Rather he conjures up to a derelict who has sunk to the lowest personal and social level. This approach makes no mention of the man proud of his desert expanses, of his tribe and lineage, of his appearance and of his valor. It leaves us with the image of a miserable creature spewn out by the desert, ragged, homeless, meek, grovelling, willing to undertake any employment for a pitiful crust of bread.

The view of the Bedouins held by travellers and caravan parties which crossed the desert generation after generation is, perhaps, the view which has become most deeply rooted among the town dwellers in Arab countries. It is a view that holds the Bedouins to be dangerous. Riding in bands, they attack, plunder and rob the caravans as they make their way through the desert, carrying goods westward. According to this view, the Bedouins are perceived as a pack of wolves, who when there are no caravans to be plundered, will attack one another. It is this view that is supported by early Arabic verses and by legends and traditions prevalent among desert tribes. Anatra is a mythological figure associated with the Arabian Peninsula of the pre-Islamic era. He and two other heroic figures, the brothers Ataya and Neami, who according to tradition fled to the Sinai after being involved in a murder in the Arabian Peninsula, spent their lives raiding and robbing, and defending themselves against the raids of other Bedouins. Their exploits have gone down in tradition as feats of courage, and to this day their figures are shrouded in an eternal aura of reverence. The Tarabbin tribe in Sinai looks upon Ataya as its spiritual father and as a great hero. His image has become sacred and he is called Sheik Ataya. His burial place in Wadi Watir, about 20 kilometers from Portuga Springs, has become a place of pilgrimage.

The prophet Mohammed strongly disapproved of this way of life which centered on robbery, plunder, and bloodshed. He preached against it vehemently and tirelessly, urging the Bedouins to forget the blood-feuds among themselves and to unite as one 'nation'. Using formidable power, and under the banner of a fervent faith, he succeeded in achieving this goal. For a brief period of time the disparate tribes united under one flag and one leader and in the Middle Ages established the mighty Arab Empire. However, those tribes that remained behind in the desert, or those which during their various conquests found themselves in deserts similar to the Arabian Peninsula, reverted to the laws of the desert.

Which of all these views is closest to the truth? I do not wish to wrong a large human community, nor do I wish to sing songs of praise. Either way would fall short of the truth. I believe there is a grain of truth in each. The Bedouins are similar to all other nomadic tribes, whether they live in the heart of the jungle or in the icy expanses of the North Pole. However, they differ in two important respects:

1. The jungle dwellers and the Eskimos wander from one place to another in pursuit of game, while the Bedouins wander through the sands in pursuit of grazing grounds. This factor places the Bedouins on a higher level of development, not unlike the American Indians, before their way of life was destroyed.

2. Unlike the Eskimos and jungle dwellers, the Bedouins have been in constant touch with advanced civilizations — those of ancient Egypt, Babylonia, the Persian Empire, the Byzantine Empire, the Arab Empire, the Egyptian Mamelukes and the Ottoman Empire. The Bedouins have had contact with various religions, mainly Christianity and Judaism, and have themselves fashioned the Moslem religion which suits them well, particularly in its elemental

nature and primeval simplicity.

But it was the desert, more than anything else, that molded the Bedouins, determined their way of life and shaped the patterns of their behavior. The Bedouins did not choose to make the desert their home. Life in the desert is life on the brink of starvation. There is a very delicate and often cruel balance between the amount of vegetation and the number of inhabitants this desert vegetation can support. In the pre-Islamic period the Bedouins maintained this balance in two ways:

1. **Limiting the birthrate.** The Bedouins of ancient times – and even their modern counterpart – were not acquainted with 20th century contraceptive measures, but they understood this important biological principle: it is the female, rather than the male, that is the source of natural increase. Accordingly, the custom of 'wad-al-bnat', or burial of daughters, became common. According to this custom a certain percentage of all female infants would be killed shortly after birth and buried, while the male infants would be cared for and allowed to grow up, to become the future providers and protectors of the tribe. The prophet Mohammed put a stop to this cruel custom and forbade it. In this connection there is a story about one of the fathers of Islam. The story is about a man who converted to Islam and was observed shortly thereafter sitting alone and alternately laughing and crying. Since this man was known for his wisdom and prudence, they wondered at his behavior and asked him what the invisible cause of his laughter and weeping was. He replied that before converting to Islam he used to worship idols fashioned with his own hands out of various materials. Once, for lack of a better material, he fashioned an idol out of fresh dates and afterwards he would bow down before it and pray. But one day when he was very hungry he ate the sacred idol.

"And why do you weep?" asked his disciples.

"I weep," replied the man, "when I remember my daughter. I had a daughter whom I loved very much, so I kept putting off killing her. I was filled with anguish, for I realized that the longer I put off killing her, the greater the wrong I would be doing both to myself and to my beloved daughter, for as she grew older she would come to understand the bitter fate that awaited her. Finally I dragged her to the spot where I planned to bury her and dug the grave while she was watching. Suddenly I felt her silken fingers on my face. She was brushing off the dirt which was caught in my beard as I was digging her grave...

I slew the daughter I loved. And now I weep at the memory of what I was forced to do by the law of necessity which prevailed in the desert."

2. **Expansion.** The second means of maintaining the delicate equilibrium between the vegetation in the barren desert and the life that it sustains was to move to areas where water was plentiful. The Bedouin has always looked covetously upon the fertile lands which hold the promise of seasonal crops. He has long suffered from poverty, hunger, the need to keep wandering in search of elusive grazing grounds, dryness, heat and cold. These have worn down his strength and shortened his life. Though he is forced to live in the desert, he has never really made peace with it. The trade caravans which passed through his native sands brought tantalizing stories of the plenty to be found beyond the desert horizon. He was aware of the existence of other ways of life, of flowing water, of fertile land, of food for man and beast available the year round. This other reality was forever stimulating his imagination. Even the prophet Mohammed was stirred by it. In his holy Koran he described the heavenly Garden of Eden in very earthy terms: A land of flowing rivers where beautiful maidens and handsome youths wander. The Bedouins had been haunted by this dream for hundreds of years before Mohammad appeared on the stage of history, and the Bedouin tribes did not wait idly for the dream to come true. In hot dry years, in times of constant hunger when the equilibrium between man and vegetation in the desert was violated, they tried their luck outside the desert, pushing towards the fertile lands blessed with water. Sometimes they would simply raid a settlement, and at other times, when little resistance was offered, they would drive out the settlers and occupy their lands. Ancient historical accounts of Iraq, the Land of Israel, and even Egypt tell of such waves of expansion rolling out of the desert. It was a life and death struggle between the settlers and the desperate nomadic raiders.

The spread of Islam and establishment of the mighty Arab Empire in the Middle Ages can, to some extent, be viewed as such a wave of expansion, but it was elaborately organized and above all, as a manifestation of fervent faith, it was inspired by a fresh new religion. It was tremendously successful. In less than a hundred years the Bedouin tribes overran Persia, Iraq, Syria, Lebanon, Sinai, Egypt, all of North Africa, and finally, with the surrender of Spain to the desert raiders, even a sizable part of Europe. It seemed that the days of the Messiah had come for the wretched Bedouins. Rich and fertile lands opened up before them. They quickly adapted to the new realities; they exchanged their camels for the swifter horse, forsook their tents and erected palaces, stopped wandering and settled down, establishing thriving villages and bustling cities. On the face of it, their suffering was over. The heavenly paradise had become a reality. They had the Tigris, the Euphrates, the Nile, wells, springs, rain and fertile land.

However, history has its irony. Precisely what seemed like an ideal and final solution to the problems of the Bedouins proved to be a calamity for those tribes that stayed behind in the desert. The successful spread of Islam, that adventurous expansionist thrust which was to have brought prosperity to the Bedouin tribes, proved to be the greatest disaster that the Bedouins met with in their long history of suffering and deprivation. The first waves of invaders established a mighty empire, stable and strong and very rich. This empire mobilized an army which no force existing at that time was strong enough to resist. The empire established itself firmly, defined its borders and defended them with exemplary efficiency. The same empire which originated with the Bedouin tribes now hermetically closed its back door to them. It established its border with the desert, drawing an impenetrable barrier between itself and any further attempts at invasion by nomads from the desert. As a precautionary measure the seat of government was established in far off Damascus, and later in well-defended Baghdad. The tribes that had remained behind in the desert felt cheated and betrayed by their brothers in the occupied lands of the empire, with their legendary wealth and their magnificent palaces. These tribes, particularly around the holy city of Mecca, the fountainhead of Islam, were the first to rebel against the Islamic empire. The revenge of the empire was swift. With an iron fist, with great cruelty and cynical disregard for the basic values of Islam, Damascus stretched forth its long arm and crushed the disgruntled desert tribes. The empire learned its lesson from this rebellion and evolved methods of preventing similar ones in the future. The Arab Empire, and later the Ottoman Empire and the Mamelukes in Egypt, sealed off the desert, imprisoning the Bedouin tribes in its great expanse. The situation which prevailed until the beginning of the 20th century was paradoxical: the very same Bedouin who seemed as free as the wind, that same nomad who wandered endlessly in the majestic expanses, that image of freedom, unfettered by land or possessions, became incarcerated in its mighty prison, unable to break out. The mighty desert had turned into a trap, and the inhabitants of Arab settlements on the desert borders, so proud of the Arab heritage handed down to them by the Bedouin tribes, came to regard the Bedouins as a potential enemy, dangerous and destructive.

Needless to say, the Bedouins who for centuries had had to endure punishments and restrictions from the countries which flourished around the desert, felt betrayed and harbored a feeling of suspicion, hostility and mistrust towards the strangers who had always been unkind. A song which Shabtai Levi took down from the Bedouins in the South Sinai expresses this feeling quite clearly:

"If anyone comes from the steep slopes,
We shall repel him in Almighty God's name.
If he comes from the Wadi,
We shall push him back in the name of God the Adored.
If he comes from above,
We'll fight him with witchcraft and magic.
If he comes from the habitations of evil,
We shall drive him off with an iron fist."

These words express the horrible conviction of being surrounded by enemies on all sides. I know of no other nomads in the world who are thus enclosed in a ring of hostility and suspicion.

But we must remember that the song expresses the collective consciousness and not necessarily that of the individual Bedouin. After all, the desert, even a 'small' desert such as the Sinai, is still a tremendous expanse of sands, hills, wadis, mountains; a variety of shapes and colors. It is a world unto itself, and the Bedouin is imbued with a deep affinity for this world. He feels that it belongs to him and that he, his family and his tribe are an integral part of it. Another important factor in shaping the consciousness of the Bedouins is the fact that the population is sparse, as in any desert, whether of snow or sand. This means that the crowded conditions of a prison are absent here. The territory of each tribe is defined, and the members of each tribe feel completely free within their territory.

Moreover, the social, political and technological changes which have taken place in the world at such an accelerated speed in the 20th century have not passed the Bedouin by, whether he lives in the Arabian Peninsula or in the Sinai. Suddenly, the desert, so poor in fertile land and sources of water that for thousands of years it could barely sustain its population, became a rich source of various minerals, changing the Bedouin's way of life and outlook. In addition, modern means of transportation and communication have begun to create cracks in the wall which isolated the Bedouins for so long, bringing about some changes in their lives. But before discussing them, we must describe the physical conditions of the Bedouin's existence in the Sinai.

The Sinai Peninsula

The importance of the Sinai Peninsula has been recognized since ancient times. It has served as a land bridge between Africa and Asia, across which campaigns of conquest and trade caravans made their way from Asia to Africa and Europe and vice versa. These campaigns and caravans probably did not enrich the inhabitants of the Sinai. All those using the desert as a passage-way preferred it to be empty or sparsely settled, so that its inhabitants would not in any way disturb the progress of caravans or hinder the campaigns of conquest. The local population of the Sinai was regarded by the peoples surrounding it as a dangerous and hostile element which must be curbed by force. To this day we find there the remains of forts and military outposts whose task it was to impose the authority of the local inhabitants. Apparently no autonomous form of government, which might have exploited the peninsula's geographic-strategic advantages for the benefit of its population, was ever established in the Sinai. Nor did the mines, discovered and worked in the time of ancient Egypt, provide any advantage for the local population, and we may assume that Egypt cruelly exploited the local manpower.

The importance of the Sinai Peninsula was enhanced with the rise of Islam and the expansion of its conquests. The Arab Empire engendered flourishing trade in North Africa, Iraq and Syria. Northern Sinai bustled with caravans carrying goods and booty from Europe, the Middle East and India. Just as important were the caravans of pilgrims which began making their way to Mecca following the rise of Islam. These caravans came from Egypt, Morocco, Tunisia, Libya, Algeria and black Moslem Africa, crossing the Red Sea and the Sinai desert on their way to the holy Kaaba shrine. These pilgrim caravans continued to cross the Sinai on their way eastward every year until the Israeli conquest of Sinai in the war of 1967. Now that the Sinai is once again under Egyptian rule, the caravans have probably resumed following the same ancient routes.

With the digging of the Suez Canal in the 19th century, the Sinai became one of the most important and sensitive areas on the map of the Middle East. Since it was opened, the Canal has served as one of the major routes of maritime transport in the world. Until World War II it was almost the only avenue of contact between Great Britain and its colonies in the east, India in particular. England has since declined in global greatness and the British Empire has disintegrated, but the importance of the Suez, which connects the Mediterranean with the Red Sea, has not diminished. On the contrary. It is through the Suez, that the abundant oil of the arab countries is transported, in giant tankers, on its way to oil-thirsty Europe. Cities such as Suez, Cantara, and Ismailiya have sprung up and flourished on the banks of the Canal. But once again the Bedouins of the Sinai have been mocked by the vicissitudes of history; for neither the flourishing cities on the banks of the canal and the amazing wealth being transported on it nor the pilgrim caravans to Mecca has brought wealth or wellbeing to the Bedouin inhabitants of the Sinai, who are still destitute and on the verge of starvation. The modern towns have been populated by Egyptians from the Egyptian heartland. A sweet freshwater canal dug alongside the Suez Canal draws its water from the distant Nile. As a result, a grotesque situation has now arisen: earlier, both banks of the Suez had been desert; now the western, African bank is green, blossoming with fruit-laden orchards and fields abundant with grain, while the eastern bank remains a wilderness of barren soil, scorched sand and salty marshlands.

Minerals

Even in ancient times, the Egyptians mined turquoise in the Sinai and they are still mining it in the Maara region. The yearly yield of manganese in the Oum Bugma region alone was a quarter of a million tons. The Sinai is also rich in other minerals such as kaolin, gypsum and coal. A considerable amount of oil has been discovered in the Sinai and off-shore near its western shores. The yearly output of this valuable liquid in the fields of Abu Rodeis, Bleim and Wadi Firan reached more than five million tons annually. However, none of these resources has been used to improve the lot of the Bedouins. This wealth has become the property of the state; i.e., Egypt, a country whose population also lives well below the poverty line. The population explosion, scant resources, backward industry, primitive agriculture, and involvement in several wars have, in the space of 40 years, turned Egypt from the most advanced and prosperous country in the Arab world into one of the poorest in the world. Therefore, the proceeds of every resource discovered in the Sinai are used to replenish the depleted government coffers. Most of the minerals are earmarked for export and the foreign currency they bring in is used to pay for imports for the residents of Egypt itself.

This, then, is the essential difference between the Bedouins of the Arabian Peninsula and the Bedouins of Sinai in the second half of the 20th century: in Saudi Arabia and in the Persian Gulf States, while the legendary oil resources are controlled by a handful of powerful individuals, most of the astounding wealth resulting from these resources remains within these countries. Despite the corruption and the conspicuous waste, the ordinary Bedouin has reaped considerable benefit from this wealth. In Kuwait 50 years ago, for instance, the sparse nomadic Bedouin population was poverty-stricken, living in dilapidated tents, plagued by hunger, thirst, disease and a harsh climate. Today, the average per capita income of this same population is the highest in the world. This does not mean that every Bedouin has become a millionaire, but it does mean that every Bedouin in Kuwait is entitled to a free education, as high as university level, a free telephone and inexpensive permanent housing. The typical Kuwait Bedouin has abandoned his tent and his camel. He now lives in an air-conditioned house and drives a luxurious American car. The Bedouin in the Sinai is not inferior to his Kuwaiti cousin in background, technical skill or intelligence; yet, if you find a Sinai Bedouin driving a luxurious American car, chances are that the car has been stolen in Israel and is on its way to a hiding place beneath some sand dune, later to be sold to a buyer from

Egypt. If the Bedouin in the Sinai touches the wealth passing through Sinai at all, it is only in the capacity of an accomplice to smugglers or as a hired-hand earning a pittance.

The amazing wealth which has flooded the Arab world since World War II, the wealth which has completely changed the face of the Middle East, the wealth which has become a major factor in international politics, the wealth which has turned the classic traditional Bedouins into frequenters of the gambling casinos of Monte Carlo and Las Vegas has completely bypassed the Bedouins of the Sinai. The wealth before which nations tremble, and sometimes grovel, the wealth which allows Bedouins to buy palaces in indignant Britain and in proud America has not reached the Sinai Bedouins. And if the Egyptian government is now building some permanent settlements and pitiful housing for the Sinai Bedouins along the northern flank of the Sinai Peninsula, it is only for reasons of prestige and security, in order not to leave a vacuum between the African part of Egypt and Israel.

Climate

The climate plays a major part not only in detemining the soil and the landscape but also in shaping the behavior and life-style of the Bedouins. The most typical climatic feature of the Sinai Peninsula is the extremity of its changes of weather. The Sinai is part of a desert chain which extends around the globe. It is flanked by vast deserts to the east and to the west. Nevertheless, it is surrounded by water, a significant factor in moderating its climate, particularly in the coastal strip along the Mediterranean. Another factor affecting the climate is the fact that the peninsula is not a uniform surface of sand. In the north, there are large areas affected by the Mediterranean where the amount of rainfall makes planned agriculture possible, assuring a livelihood for the local inhabitants. In the south, there are high mountains, more than 2,000 meters above sea level, with an average annual rainfall of 10 mm. as compared to 100 mm. in the north. Judged by its average temperatures, too, the Sinai seems to typify desert conditions. In January the daily maximum is 18–20 degrees Centigrade and the daily minimum is 2–8 degrees. In the summer months, the daily temperatures are between a low of 16 degrees and a high of 36 degrees. However, the climate does not always conform to the average. Temperature may rise to a high of 44 degrees and fall to a low of 15 below zero. And in winter, snow-covered mountaintops are by no means uncommon. In other words, this desert is both scorching and freezing, and the Bedouins must maneuver between the two extremes. But that is not all. Average rainfall statistics notwithstanding, the weather sometimes goes mad and the entire annual rainfall pours down in a single day. Such a situation makes any substantial planned agriculture virtually impossible. The Bedouins thus suffer from long droughts on one hand, and from another of nature's destructive forces – floods – on the other hand. When such a large amount of water, in terms of the desert, pours down in a single day, mighty torrents stream down the mountain slopes dislodging boulders, uprooting trees, sweeping away tent encampments, killing man and beast. Not every Bedouin, like the one mentioned in the anecdote earlier, has a transistor radio, and even if he did, he would still often be surprised by the calamitous floods, since forecasts in an area of such capricious weather are nor reliable. The destructive force of flooding is deeply imprinted on the consciousness of the Bedouins. Following is a passage from a novel by this writer, describing the catastrophe of flood.

The story involves a man from Upper Egypt who, after committing a murder, flees his village, taking his baby with him. Feeling unsafe in Egypt, he decides to walk to Palestine, along the railroad tracks in the northern Sinai.

"Standing on the railroad track from the east, he realized that no such death had lain in wait for him on his long trek down the Nile. Water. He had no water. A Bedouin, he said to himself, doesn't die of thirst. He passed his tongue over his parched lips, trying to puzzle out this riddle. 'Maybe the Bedouin can smell water from afar,' he said aloud. He didn't care if the little child woke now. In his despair, he didn't even care if the whole desert came alive and those murdering bands which he was so afraid of appeared from behind the hills of sand. But he couldn't free himself of the nagging thought: "How could it be that I, who had grown up surrounded by an abundance of water, by canals and a river as wide as the sea, was unable to smell water from several steps away while the Bedouin, who grew up in this terrible dryness, could locate a waterhole by the quiver of his sand-clogged nostrils. It was one of God's mysteries."

He raised his accusing eyes to heaven and was about to begin an uncompromising quarrel with the Creator. But he ended up mocking himself: 'Your mouth is dry as sand, your tongue is stuck to your gums, and you still want to argue with God?'

His father had been a pious man, in his own fashion, and it might have been expected that some of his father's religion, with its emphasis on the miraculous and glorification of miracles, would rub off on him. But he had never yielded to believing in miracles. He was a Christian Copt from Upper Egypt. If he had been a Moslem, things would have been different. A Moslem would put his trust in God and accept his fate. To him everything is preordained. But all the important things that he, Ibrahim, had wanted in life, happened because he had wanted them to happen. Sometimes he had even tempted fate a little. He did not expect any heavenly help then, though there was a moment of weakness when he did hope for God's intervention. That was when, brushing the sleeping baby's face with his lips, he realized that this was no ordinary sleep. His son was dying. He thought to smooth a spot in the sand, place his baby on it, retreat a step or two, and place the reponsibility for the fate that vanquished him with God. But no matter how hard he tried, the words of a fitting appeal to God somehow eluded him.

The distant horizon and the endless rails leading to the sunrise intensified his despair. The baby's breathing was fitful, as if his tiny body was rejecting the dry, cold air. Finally, Ibrahim made up his mind that he would do it. He left the tracks, set his son down on the lifeless sand and returned to the tracks. Fixing his green eyes on the distant point where the two rails met, and pressing his arms to his body, he resolved that he would cast a magic spell on the railroad. He would shorten the tracks, he would compress them, turning them into a convenient bridge that would take him to the Holy Land before the sun rose. He shut his eyes and relaxed his stomach muscles to prepare himself for this mighty effort. Patiently he waited for tranquility to descend on him, for that deep peace without which no spell can be cast. Tranquility came, deep and pure, bestowing strength and faith, like an awakening. Then he opened his eyes and commanded the tracks to obey his will.

The answer came from an unexpected direction. Far to the south, thundering flames lit up the edges of the canopy of heaven. The abysmal roar was so mighty that he imagined the foot of some Titan kicking at the mountains and rolling them like pebbles in the wilderness. He stood transfixed. From the corner of his eye he watched the flashes cleaving the skies and fearlessly addressed the Almighty. 'I told you I would not budge until the tracks shrank. You can roar all you want, but save him I will. I will save my son from Death's claws.'

In the course of the war between himself and God, the stars had fled for their lives. He was sure of it. The sky was pitch black. Again and again God wielded his whips of fire across the dome of the sky but Ibrahim had more courage than the stars. He waited for God to finish his communication so that he could again gather his psychic powers to subdue the tracks. While he was making his third attempt to do this the earth began to tremble and quake beneath his feet. He closed his eyes happily, thinking that his spell had succeeded, but when he opened them he was bitterly disappointed. The tracks had not shrunk. They still stretched towards infinity. Something had gone wrong in his confrontation with God. Maybe God was too strong for him, maybe the devil was mocking him, or maybe he had been weakened and his strength had forsaken him when he left his native village.

The heavens calmed and a few hesitant stars peered out. But now there was a different kind of noise, a strange rumbling that seemed to come from the bowels of the earth. Even the wooden ballast on which he was standing shook. Jumping up, he grabbed the swooning baby but did not know where to run. The noise was closing in on him. He was a man who had lived all his life in an arid region and had never witnessed any substantial generosity from the clouds. So he had no way of knowing that a rainstorm was in progress not far away and that an enormous flood was about to wash through the desert, cutting deep channels, demolishing high hills, uprooting trees and carrying off even the railroad tracks.

He hurried to the highest hill to see what fate awaited him — whether God's punishment or the devil's mockery. At that moment he was struck by the thought that he was witnessing a natural phenomenon that he had never experienced before. He looked up and saw the stars turning brighter. This did not calm him. They twinkled with wicked malice, and the earth continued to tremble beneath his feet.

'So be it. This is where we'll be buried,' he said aloud to the unconscious infant in his arms. He even thought of getting down on his knees to dig a grave wide enough for his body and that of his son. He looked up at the merciless raging sky, 'but who will cover us?'

He thought he heard the gallop of horses, thousands of horses galloping across the desert. Convinced that he was caught in a great Bedouin raid, he huddled on the hill, trying to conceal his large body. The infant's breathing was like a dying flame now. With two fingers he opened his son's parched lips, bent over him and tried to revive him with his own saliva. He knew that by doing so he was hastening his own death, but for reasons he did not quite understand, he wished that he and his son would breathe their last together. He felt the desire to give his own body's life-giving fluid to his son. He raked his tongue with his teeth, squeezing until he realized that it was not saliva he was transferring to his son's mouth, but blood.

The noise grew louder. He shook his head. 'No,' he said indifferently. 'It's not horses.'

The infinite space of the desert seemed to be engulfing him in turmoil. 'That's good,' he tried to comfort himself. 'This is a great earthquake. Those hills will be moved in our direction and will cover us. What nicer burial could a man wish for?'

Suddenly his nostrils came alive. At first he didn't dare trust his sense of smell, but his ears too picked up the sound of raging water. He sprang up, crying 'Son, the Nile's blessing has overtaken us. Our river has followed us!'

But the Nile had never flowed with such speed. He squinted trying to make out the railroad in the dark. It was no longer there. Ibrahim whispered to his son 'The hill we are standing on is like a boat in the middle of the sea.'

Some moments passed before he dared to express the joy welling up within him. Then, shouting for joy like a child, he ran down the hill. 'Son, water! Water! Water!'

He waited eagerly for sunrise because he wanted to see the baby's eyes. 'The eyes tell all,' he said to himself. He held the baby up high so that his eyes would catch the first sunrays. He smiled gratefully when he saw a light in the baby's black eyes. Then, he knelt and buried his face in the baby's tiny chest and, overcome with shame, he wept.

He went down the hill to the newly transformed desert, to the turbid water, and washed his face. He looked at the raised road bed on which the rails had been laid. It looked like the ruins of some wall. In certain spots the embankment had been swept away together with the rails and in others, there were large gaps, leaving the rails stretched over an abyss, like a bare bridge. He looked around him in wonder for a long time, and it was a while before he sensed that strange eyes were fixed on his back. He spun around like a startled animal and saw before him a Bedouin with a shapeless wet bundle on his back.

'Where did you find him?' asked the Bedouin.

He was afraid to answer because he knew that his sing-song Egyptian accent would give away his origin.

'The boy,' explained the Bedouin.

Ibrahim noticed the sadness in the Bedouin's voice. He was tall and gaunt, and Ibrahim saw that he was beyond exhaustion. He stood there like a shadow, lacking almost any substance, except for his weary voice and the strange wet bundle on his back. 'The boy?' asked Ibrahim, feigning stupidity.

The Bedouin was silent. Perhaps he was no longer curious or else he needed all his strength to remain standing. With a strange movement he turned mutely eastward. His feet moved as if obeying an order from which there was no escape. His head inclined forward, as if pulled by an invisible rope towards an undesirable destination.

In the hush that settled over the puddles of water which remained after the flood, objects were robbed of their natural shape and appearance. Branch-tops were planted in the mud, while roots reached up towards an indifferent sky. Decapitated hills cast black shadows not typical of the desert. The carcass of a goat was lying on its back in the silt and the animal's ears were stretched forward as if it had frozen while leaping back. In this hallucinatory scene Ibrahim found his feet obeying the rhythm of the Bedouin's gait. He had made up his mind to keep quiet but the words seemed to escape his mouth. 'He is my own son, I swear it.'

'He is alive,' the Bedouin said in his weary voice.

'I saved him at the last moment. We thank God for the flood he sent us.'

'God's name be praised,' murmured the Bedouin.

Ibrahim recognized the tone of voice in which the words of thanksgiving were uttered. He shuddered and was again filled with suspicion. The voice expressed outward and false acceptance of a situation that was hard to accept. The Bedouin's silence became oppressive. 'This is my own son,' Ibrahim repeated with defiant emphasis.

'You are lucky,' the Bedouin answered, adding dryly, 'God loves you.'

'Me?'

'Your son is alive, isn't he?'

They were both trudging barefoot in the mud.

Ibrahim tried to conceal the great strength in his body from the Bedouin. He deliberately lagged behind the exhausted Bedouin because he trusted no one, certainly not a barefooted Bedouin who materialized like a shadow out of the murderous wilderness. They both climbed the embankment and walked along the railroad tracks, their torn feet crushing the gravel. The bundle on the Bedouin's back aroused Ibrahim's curiosity, but he didn't want to ask any questions. The bundle was wrapped in a shapeless keffia. It was only then that he noticed that the Bedouin was bare-headed. One corner of the keffia was pulled over his right shoulder, another corner passed under the armpit of his left arm, and the edges were tied in a rough knot across the Bedouin's chest. A trickle of muddy liquid streaked down his back from the mud covered cloth. The mark it left on the gelabbia was soon dried by the blazing sun.

Ibrahim looked hard at the bundle and almost choked. His fear grew and he wished he could get away from the Bedouin. Now he was afraid that his son would wake. A baby's voice might sound eerie in the gloomy silence that swallowed their plodding footsteps. The Bedouin walked silently in front of him, obeying the unseen rope that was pulling him eastward.

'They are capable of kidnapping', Ibrahim nursed a sullen hostility in his heart to suppress another feeling. 'These robbers are capable of anything.' But the other feeling would not go away. 'All their lives they deal in robbery and murder.'

Strange circumstances had forced him to become a father. A fierce love blossomed and burned in his heart, flame upon flame, till it culminated in this snippet of life in his arms. He felt that thanks to the tiny body, growing even while it was sleeping in his arms, he was becoming a different person. With fear and pride in his heart, with joy and hope, with pleasure and pain he had crossed half the desert, bearing a new life eastward, and now here was Death walking in front of him. He had never experienced such conflicting feelings. From his experience in the harsh world in which he had grown up, he knew that feeling compassion was like trusting people blindly. A person whose pain you share might exploit your weakness, catch you off-guard, not armed with that effective weapon, suspicion. Nevertheless compassion welled up in his heart like an open wound, like a consuming flame.

In the heavy silence he continued to stride behind the exhausted Bedouin. 'I'll tell him I'm tired,' Ibrahim thought. 'Why must I drag after him? Soon the baby will wake and want to eat. And the Bedouin will stand and watch. He will drop his dead bundle in my lap and rob me of my...'

A hatred as fierce as a desert storm extinguished all compassion.

'His poor mother,' the Bedouin said in his dry voice.

'She is not dead?'

The Bedouin did not sense the hatred. He turned his head and his reddened eyes rested listlessly on Ibrahim's face. 'No, she's alive.' He didn't stop walking. The words poured out of his mouth in a monotonous tone, like the gravel crunching under his feet. 'She was barren. For many years she was barren. Do you have any tobacco? I lost mine while I was looking for the child's body in the darkness of the flood.'

Continuing to walk, he stuffed his clay pipe. He inhaled deeply and a smile of pleasure fleetingly crossed his colorless face. Ibrahim listened in impermeable silence.

'I paid thirty camels for a young woman. My first wife refused to accept this situation. She made life unbearable for both me and herself. I've never seen a woman like that, who refuses to accept her fate,' he openly expressed his admiration and affection. 'A stubborn woman, capable of scratching heaven's face to ask for God's protection. What could I do? I did not entirely abandon her cheerless tent. When the young one became pregnant she was furiously jealous. Can you believe such things, man? She commanded her womb and it returned to life. It is as if in nothing but sand, with not a drop of water, suddenly an orchard bloomed. I wish you could have seen what a handsome child she bore. Because of him I forgot the tent of the young one. The older one would strut around with one breast bared, the nipple between the baby's ruby lips, and proclaim in a voice loud enough to reach the young one's ears that she was suckling honey and not just milk. And the baby's cheeks really did take on the color of honey. Where were you standing when the flood struck? We were camping in the dry bed of the stream. This was no ordinary flood. The earth melted and flowed beneath our feet, as if frightened. With her screams still echoing in my ears I pursued the flood that had taken my son.'

Mutely Ibrahim handed the tobacco pouch and the clay pipe to the Bedouin who accepted the gesture gratefully. He felt he must return the kindness. 'You have obviously walked a long way.'

'Yes.'

'And how will you feed your son till you reach the place you're going? Does he have any teeth?'

'He has a few. I chew dates for him and then put them in his mouth.'

'You'll find plenty of milk in my encampment.'

And so Ibrahim followed the Bedouin who had Death dangling from his back.''

The Bedouins are nomadic tribes; continual migration from place to place is the basic feature of their way of life. They are always emotionally prepared to fold up their tents, gather their scant belongings and head for more promising horizons.

More than anything else, it is the desert that shapes the Bedouin's character and determines his patterns of behavior. The place where a Bedouin pitches his tent is not a matter of free choice. It is the place where he has managed to find the delicate and sometimes very cruel balance between the quantity of water and vegetation and the number of inhabitants they can sustain. It is a balance that can only be arrived at by wandering.

Just as an Englishman's home is his castle, so too the concept of private boundaries is sacred to the Bedouin, whether he owns a lowly bower or a tent. On his summer wanderings, the Bedouin does not take his heavy winter tent along. He folds it and uses it to store whatever household items he does not need. Since this unguarded property is bound to lure thieves, especially where poverty and want are so common, a system of laws, involving very stiff fines, has been developed as a deterrent to potential offenders.

Once the house has been loaded onto
the camel, the rest of the family is free to
wander in search of a new "address".

''The days of plenty are over.
The summer sun is blazing
and I am yet to find my beloved.
The days of plenty are past
and I am faced with the distant
grazing lands of summer.''

A nomad's life is a never-ending search for grazing lands for his herd. The wife is responsible for making sure that the flocks are tended to. In the Southern Sinai it is the young girls of the family who become the shepherdesses. After she marries, the Bedouin woman no longer goes off with the flocks. Rather she stays in her tent. Thus, the daughter becomes the shepherdess but the mother's expertise is such that she still remains the authority on managing the herd. The young daughter, off in the mountains and far away from the home tent, is a cause of concern to her family, which worries that she might be faced with temptation. As for the shepherdesses themselves, they in fact await any suitors who may come along. Despite the strict prohibitions, desires are often stronger and love does blossom in the desert. Thanks to a kind of solidarity that prevails in the desert, one shepherdess will virtually never inform on another.

A large flock usually means that several families' animals have been put together. This arrangement solves the problem of families that have no daughters and also frees more of the women to help with the housework.

"When she walked past me
in her fringed scarf
she carried my small heart
in the palm of her hand."

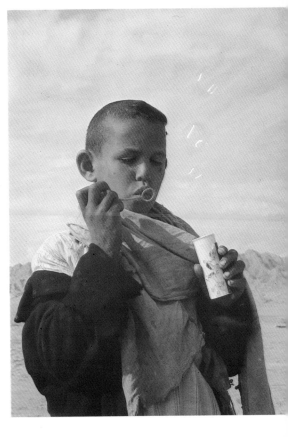

"For ninety nights I suffer the pangs of love
and if I die it will be because of her.
How I wish I had not come down to the well today,
For I came up from the well and I am still thirsty."

The wife is responsible for the family's
water supply. The mother on the right is
teaching her daughter how to draw
water. The well is the women's gathering
point. It also gives the men a rare
opportunity to watch the young girls
from afar.

On the look-out for a prospective husband... maybe?
These young ladies have come of age. All are single, mature young women. The one with the white beads around her hair line has been declared by her family as available for marriage; the other two are still ''ladies in waiting'' for parental approval. The black veil symbolizes a sharp turn in the girl's life, indicating her physical readiness for marriage and childbearing.

Desert elegance – a lady's foot ▶ ornamented with jewelry.

Strolling the desert in black
Black is the dominant color worn by the
Bedouin girl and woman, as it is the color
that stands out best against the yellow
background of the desert. To be seen in
the vast landscape may be crucial to
survival.

Attending to her family's needs for warmth and protection.
It is the woman who supplies the family with warmth and protection from the desert cold. The woman or her daughter goes out to collect dry branches to be used for heat, light, and cooking fuel.

Shepherdesses meeting in the desert.
A girl's responsibility for the family flock begins at a young age and ends with her marriage. The shepherdess is often utterly alone in remote places and passes the time singing and playing the flute. A meeting in the desert is a real joy...

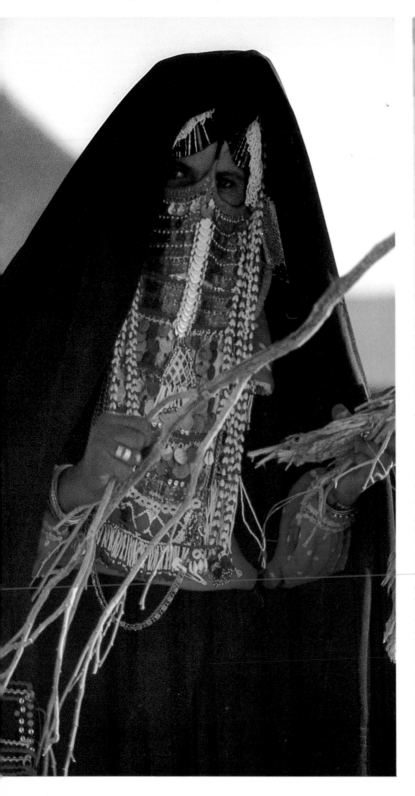

The Tribe

The tribal framework of the Bedouins is firmly established, closely knit and very rigid. The Bedouin takes pride in his tribe and jealously guards its status among other tribes. The tribal framework directly affects family life, where the framework is just as rigid as in the tribe. Why is this so?

Very few nomads in the world have established such an elaborate tribal system. The American Indians had one somewhat similar to that of the Bedouins. When they settled on fertile lands with plenty of water and had large herds, they needed the tribal structure to help protect the natural wealth that surrounded them. Many coveting eyes waited for a moment of weakness as an opportunity to attack, and only a well organized tribe could fight back.

But no one coveted the Bedouin's sweltering desert. The enemies that surrounded him on all sides rather than scheming to rob him of something they lacked, feared him. Since the need for self-defense can be ruled out as the causes of tribal organization, the assumption held by certain sociologists sounds convincing. Namely, that life in the desert, with its constant struggle against the powers of nature requires large-scale cooperation and unity. On his own, the Bedouin would not be able to accomplish certain tasks such as digging and maintaining a well.

This assumption seems questionable. The Bedouins have not erected walls or undertaken any other great project which would require a large well-organized force to establish and defend it. The importance of the tribe goes well beyond that of a well, even if we assume that the well is the only source of life in the waterless desert. The Bedouin tribe evolved, organized and perfected itself not as a building force but as a fighting force. The supreme function of the tribe is to defend its members when it is weak and to carry out sorties of pillage and plunder when it is strong. Despite the desert's vastness there has never been room in it for a dense population. And the Bedouin, no matter how industrious and persevering he was, would never be able to eat his fill without sticking his hand into the pot of the neighboring tribe. It was the imperative of the cruel desert, and it alone, that gave rise to the tribe. Even the names used in the tribe to describe its hierarchical organization suggest military organization. The basic cell in the tribe is, of course, the family. The family unit contains the head of the family, his wife or wives, his daughters, his sons, and their wives. The kinship group, that is uncles, cousins and other relatives, is known as "Homs", meaning a fifth. A larger unit, containing several "fifths" is the "quarter" and the quarters unite to make up the tribe. Only a military organization would make such subdivision necessary. Historically, the tribe was established as a military force. A Bedouin who is not a member of a tribe is vulnerable and defenseless. It is the custom for such a man to seek the protection of a strong tribe, for himself and his family, by requesting permission to join it. Even today, when a Bedouin loses his temper in a fight with another Bedouin, he doesn't think of himself as an individual in conflict with another individual. He carefully considers the strength of his tribe as compared to that of his adversary's before doing anything hasty.

The fact that the tribal framework constitutes the source of the individual's strength guarantees the continuity of traditional Bedouin society and guards it against the vicissitudes of time. However, we must not view Bedouin society as a haven unaffected and unsullied by modern life. We must distinguish between the standard of living, which changes, and the way of life and social structure, which have not been substantially affected. Mahmoud, the basket weaver from A-Tur put it well when he said, "There were the Turks, then the British, then the Egyptians and then the Israelis. They all came and went. Only two things remained unchanged – the Bedouins and the desert. And that is the source of our strength." Mahmoud the Bedouin said this to Israeli Shlomo Arad when the latter came to say goodbye to him before the Sinai was returned to Egyptian rule.

The frequent changes of rule combined with difficult

ecological conditions have made the Bedouin a tolerant and adaptable person. The Moslem religion, with its emphasis on fatalism, has also contributed to these qualities. This has produced the mistaken impression that the Bedouin is giving up his traditional way of life in favor of progress. What is closer to the truth is that the Bedouin is trying to make his daily life a bit easier but because he is aware of the transience of whatever situation he finds himself in, he clings to his traditional way of life as the source of his enduring power to survive.

Just how did the foreign presence affect the Bedouins? I shall deal with the period of Israeli rule in the Southern Sinai (1967–1979), based on the experiences and impressions of Shlomo Arad, who stayed in the area for long periods of time.

"I remember how appalled I was when I first saw Bedouin children drinking Coca Cola, Bedouin youths riding camels while listening to transistor radios and Bedouin men wearing western clothes. I thought 'We've come to a reservation and we are ruining it'. It took me many years to realize where the source of the Bedouin's strength lay and how superficial these changes were. Perhaps this will serve to illustrate:

When the deadline for the evacuation drew near, I went down to the Sinai on a farewell journey, to say goodbye to people who at first had been so strange to me, so different in mentality and way of life, and who had become friends. One of these, who was a close friend, was Hader. I had met Hader 13 years before, a young man wearing the traditional Gelabia. He owned three camels and his main occupation was drinking tea and coffee, alternately. Now Hader spoke Hebrew fluently, wore fashionable jeans and was working as a skilled auto mechanic. Seemingly this was a man who had forsaken the past and was confidently taking his place in the 20th century. But the change was only superficial. For I had never spoken to his wife alone, and even in her own home she had never been asked to join the men for an afternoon cup of tea. On this last day of my stay at the encampment she handed her husband some dry dates so that he could present them to me as her farewell gift. When I was leaving, she raised her hand in farewell, from a distance, calling, 'God be with you'. After 13 years, no meeting of the eyes, no handshake.

Most interesting, and revealing, was my reunion with my friends on the occasion of President Sadat's visit in the region of the Saint Catherine monastery, which I was covering as a photo-journalist. I met many friends, people at whose table I had eaten and in whose tents I had slept only a few short weeks earlier. Now they were all in traditional dress, paying homage to their new ruler. Not only was I not invited to their homes this time, but I wasn't even greeted. A stranger would not understand such behavior and would assume that the Bedouins were hypocritical and disloyal. The very fact that this behavior did not surprise me and that I took it for granted made me feel that I really knew the Bedouins well. 'The king is dead – long live the new king'. The Bedouin knows that as of this day he must live under the rule of a new 'king' and accept his authority. Real loyalty is reserved only for those who share his fate – his tribesmen. All other relationships are transient."

With the Israeli occupation, the Sinai was flooded with Israeli soldiers, researchers and hikers as well as tourists from Europe and the United States. These did not come riding on camels to be received as guests in the tradition of Bedouin hospitality; they came as masters demanding service and willing to pay for it in cash. Once again the Bedouin proved how quickly he could adapt himself to a new situation and turn it to his advantage to improve his standard of living. He turned to occupations such as waiter, cook and tourist guide. Yet he preserved his identity and his way of life. The Bedouin's adaptability must not be mistaken for self-effacement before western culture. It is the Bedouin who decides the nature of the encounter between his culture and the others with which he periodically comes in contact. The innate autonomy which is an inherent feature of Bedouin character is not undermined by changes in his standard of living, all the more so since these changes often prove to be temporary.

There have been some isolated cases of young Bedouin men who formed relationships with tourists from abroad. It is significant that in all such known cases, it was the women who became integrated into Bedouin society; the men did not leave their tribe. These alliances have had no emotional, cultural or familial effects on Bedouin society, beyond the effect on the individuals involved.

For many generations the Sinai Peninsula has been a

frontier separating hostile forces. In the second half of the 20th century the area became a 'hot spot' because of the wars fought there between Egypt and Israel. While these two hostile camps were fighting with pitiless fury, killing and destroying, while the desert was strewn with the remains of soldiers and of military waste, the Bedouins, who were formally Egyptian citizens, stood by as observers. Furthermore, they were perhaps the only population on earth which remained unharmed while its territory served as the battlefield in a series of bitter wars. And when the victors – whether Israelis or Egyptians – arrived, the Bedouins did everything they could to curry favor.

Another factor which has adversely affected the life of the Bedouins in the Sinai is smuggling. The Sinai is surrounded by countries which have put up strict customs barriers. It is also an important stop on the route where drugs, especially hashish, are smuggled between the producing countries and the consumer-countries, particularly Egypt. Drug-smuggling nowadays is a sophisticated operation requiring absolute secrecy, persistence and loyalty to those in charge. Quite a few Bedouins have joined smuggling rings, and for the first time in their lives they must now prove their loyalty to an authority outside the tribe. However, the Bedouin owed true allegiance to his tribe alone, no matter what outside contacts he had. In the course of thousands of years no foreign rule had succeeded in breaking this tribal loyalty and transferring it to any other institution. It was the dream of the prophet Mohammed, his great vision, to break this tribal loyalty and to instill a sense of national allegiance in its place. But he failed. The Bedouin paid lip service to the new religion; he accepted it because it was easier to accept than any other religion and because it held the promise of an empire. Even when the Empire was established the Bedouin's loyalty was first and foremost to his tribe.

Relations between the Bedouins and the representatives of the foreign ruler are clear and well defined. Bedouin society as a whole has a common interest and is united against the foreign rule and its laws. Any Bedouin who cooperates with it against another Bedouin is considered an informer and his act an act of treachery – 'Fat'na'.

Many cases are known of trials before tribal judges in which one Bedouin accuses another of informing on him to the authorities and causing his home to be searched for hashish or government property. The injured party claims violation of the honor of his house, the honor of his wife, and blood-laws. The accused can prove his innocence only through 'bish'a'.

'Bish'a' means that the accused must touch a heated iron with his tongue. If he touches it and is not burned his innocence is proven, but any reluctance to touch it is taken as an admission of guilt.

Loyalty and devotion to the tribe are a supreme value. They are above any considerations of religion, patriotism and citizenship. Although I do not wish to liken the Bedouins to the Mafia, this tribal loyalty is very similar to the loyalty existing in the Mafia in Sicily. It is possible that due to the proximity between southern Italy and the Bedouins of Northern Africa, the Mafia borrowed this admirable custom, which was originally meant to protect the community from hostile strangers.

Given such a relationship between the tribe and the individual, ostracism by the tribe is the greatest calamity that can befall a Bedouin. It is the severest punishment that Bedouin society can impose on one of its members. In a society where all punishments are economic rather that corporeal (there is no capital punishment), ostracism is a kind of death sentence, since it really amounts to expulsion from the framework of collective tribal responsibility. A banished person is not to be helped in time of trouble and his property, his person or even his survival cannot be guaranteed. The severity of this punishment is borne out by its name in Arabic – "tashmis", which comes from the word "Shams", or sun, and means that the banished person is abandoned, like one left exposed to the sun. Such exposure, in the desert, is fatal.

Banishment is never imposed on a woman.

Even in cases where the banished person leaves his tribe and succeeds in establishing himself in a different society, he still views his banishment as a severe punishment and an indelible stigma. Avi Perevolotsky gives a typical example of such a case in his "Aspects of Bedouin Judicial Practice in Southern Sinai":

"A young man of the Jabeliya tribe, Farhan Salem Abu-Majbal, was ostracized from his tribe after being accused of theft and rape, and is now living in Eilat and doing very well there.

In the spring of 1979 an attempt was made to bring the banished Farhan back into the tribal fold. The man who served as mediator between Farhan and his tribe was Faraj Harb, a Bedouin who had been smuggling hashish for many years and had become poor since the Israeli rule in Sinai. Reliable sources claim that Faraj was not acting as mediator out of the goodness of his heart, but because Farhan had promised him a tidy sum if the mediation was successful. After gaining some public support, Faraj came to talk to the sheik about the matter. The sheik gathered Farhan's clique within the tribe, the Olad Slim group, who hadn't reached agreement on the matter even among themselves, and said:

'If you have more money than you need, do as you please. If you don't, listen to me.'

His meaning was quite clear. A person who wishes to be reinstated in his tribe must first be 'cleared'; i.e., all the fines imposed on him for whatever crimes he committed during his banishment must be paid. Since Farhan was no saint, he had accumulated a large sum in fines and those who wished to clear his name would first have to 'clear' his fines.

The sheik then continued, 'If Faraj's motives are honorable, let him prove it. Let him give his daughter in marriage to Farhan and let the child born to them live with the Olad Slim. After we have seen what the child is like, we will clear the father.' When the Olad Slim had heard the terms, they understood the hint and empowered the sheik to announce their objection to reinstating Farhan."

Since the Bedouin's personal security depends on the power and prestige of the tribe he belongs to, he exhibits great pride in his tribe and is forever trying to exalt its reputation. This gave rise to two genres of poetry which flourished in the pre-Islamic period and in the period immediately following the spread of Islam. One was the poetry of 'exaltation', in which the poet praises his tribe, enumerates its virtues and its feats in the battlefield, and notes its generosity and hospitality and the terror it strikes in the hearts of its enemies. The other was the poetry of 'deprecation', in which the poet mocks the rival tribes and shows his contempt in rhetorical exaggeration.

Hospitality is not just a nice custom practiced by the Bedouins. A Bedouin proud of his descent looks upon hospitality as an innately Arab trait and tries to cultivate it.

Very few Bedouins perceive the existential significance of hospitality. This custom exists among Eskimos as well. The fierce polar cold can be fatal to a lone wayfarer who finds no shelter. Therefore hospitality in the polar region is a matter of life and death, and the Eskimo goes out of his way to make his guest comfortable and his stay pleasant, and even goes so far as to offer him his wife to keep him warm. The desert sun and the danger of dehydration in the desert can be just as fatal as the polar ice. A Bedouin who does not offer his hospitality to a wandering nomad is sentencing him to a terrible death.

The theme of hospitality is reflected in Bedouin poetry. The poet praising his tribe proclaims that each night his tribesmen light bonfires near the entrance to their tents in order to attract anyone wandering in the vicinity. On the other hand, when the poet is denouncing the rival tribe he claims that its members go so far as to put out their cooking fires when they hear steps approaching. One poet, who went to great lengths to denounce the rival tribe, wickedly stressed the miserliness of its members by claiming that they even begrudge the water necessary to put out their fires and instead they send their women out to urinate on them.

Much of the woman's time is spent in and around her "kitchen" – an undefined corner in the family tent. The main staple of the Bedouin diet is rice and "fatir" (bread); only on rare, festive occasions is meat served. The wife sits by the fire for hours, preparing the family's food and tea, a position to be envied in the cool of winter, but pitied during the long months of the summer heat. The "lucky" ones can share the work – sharing the same husband, the two wives also divide the kitchen chores between them.

Mother Earth

Bearing children is the most important role of the Bedouin wife. It makes for a strong family and enhances the woman's position in the home. Bedouin mothers and babies share a loving relationship filled with physical contact. Small babies nurse until their mother's next pregnancy – at least two and sometimes four years. Babies are encouraged to explore their immediate world, which brings them into direct knowledge of the activities of Bedouin life.

Last touches of make-up before her husband arrives.
In addition to the physical demands of her role as wife and mother, the Bedouin woman is attentive to her appearance.

Young boys stay close to their mothers, who shower them with love and affection. The self-confidence of adulthood, so badly needed in the Bedouin is reinforced during these formative years.

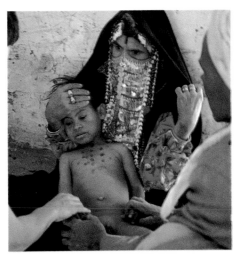

To his children, the father stands for physical safety. He is more attached to his sons than to his daughters and serves as a model for them to emulate. In times of crisis it is the father who is the backbone of the family. Above: A mongoloid child was treated by body burns in the hope of expelling the "evil eye"; the father is there to comfort the mother and child.

An intimate moment in the tent-site.

Sheik Day

The graves of sheiks are to be found throughout the Southern Sinai. They are a destination for pilgrimages. Religious ceremonies held at the grave-sites serve as occasions for social gatherings as well. The importance of the ''Zoara'' lies in the opportunity it offers the Bedouins to congregate after living in isolation all year. The event lasts several days. Each family pitches its tent and invites its relations and friends. The festive meals are the highlight of the occasion, a rarity enjoyed only on Sheik Days or weddings.
Left: After the slaughter, families heading for the tent to prepare the feast.

The highlight of the Sheik Day celebrations is the sacrificial offering. It is also a rare opportunity to eat meat, an item not normally included in the Bedouin diet. Only the men take part in the slaughter. The number of animals slaughtered as an offering symbolizes the Bedouin's wealth and position in the eyes of his fellow-tribesmen. The slaughtering is performed near the sheik's grave and from there each family head takes his offering to the family tent-site for the festive meal.

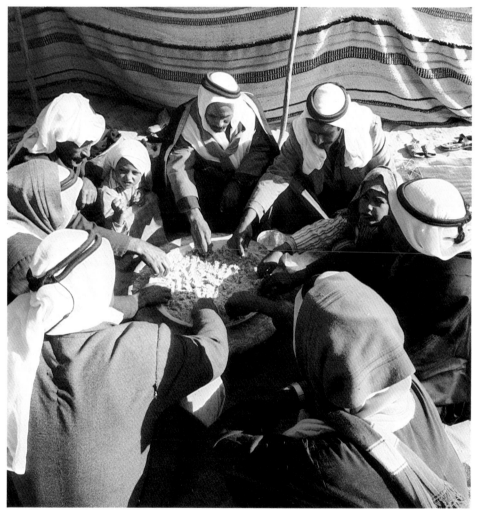

"There can be no treachery after people have broken bread together."

During Sheik Days, it is the men who do the cooking and the baking. A family invites relatives and friends for a joint celebration. The men eat first, as the women sit in the back. Whatever is left is for the children and the women.

"Although you are the one who came to us
Although you are the one who visits us
Although you are the one who bestows
respect upon our home
May it be known: we are the guests
and you are the master of the house!"

Celebrating

During "Zoara", women join in the "Dahyayyah" dance, the sole opportunity for them to "show themselves off" in front of strange men. While the men stand in a row facing a woman, she shows off her beauty by the movements of her body under her robes. The excitement of the men often leads to sexual tension, which may in turn lead to problems and at times to tragic solutions. But all the same, the husband has no say during the event itself, and the woman has a rare night of free expression.

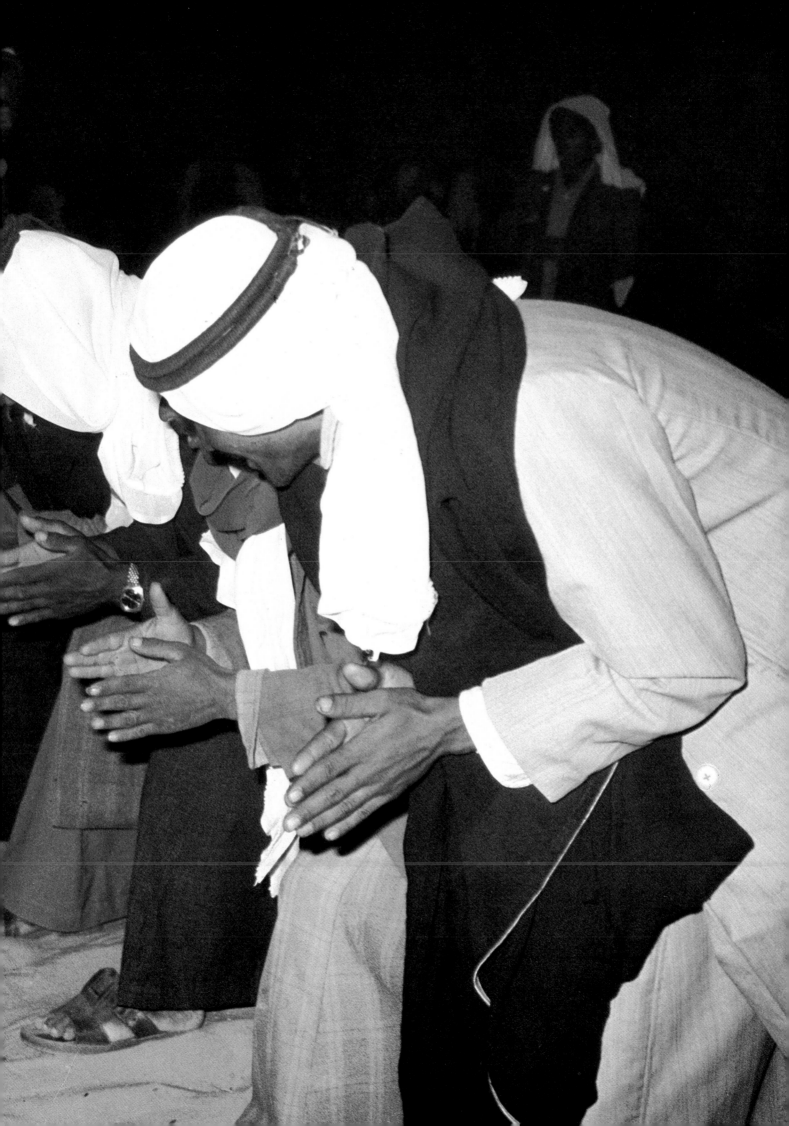

The Bedouin depends on his camel, a source of pride and wealth. The very same animal which many regard as clumsy, capricious and ugly figures in the Bedouin mind as a beautiful creature, graceful, gentle and loyal. The Bedouin man's attitude to his body and attire is modest, even ascetic. Whatever luxury and adornment he spares himself, however, is lavished on his camel. The saddle is of the finest leather. The camel is covered with colorful beads and tassels and attractive harnesses. The camel is pampered and revered.

*"If you have invited a Bedouin through
the entrance to your home,
Widen it so that his camel too may
enter."*

Farming in the Southern Sinai is based
on oasis and their sources of water.
Flood agriculture is nonexistent here
because of the strong and destructive
currents. In the oasis, palm trees, various
fruit trees and irrigated vegetables are
grown, along with other annual growths
like tobacco and wheat.
The Bedouins still use the ancient
methods of separating the grains from
the chaff.

Market-Day

The Bedouins do not grow most of their food. Rather, their isolation makes it necessary for them to make long trips to shopping areas. Market days are an opportunity to meet for commercial as well as social purposes. Transactions on market days are extremely varied. Vegetables, sheep, gold and fabric all change hands, and sometimes there may be some matchmaking as well.

The "rababa" on the right and the "sumsumiyah" on the left are string instruments which accompany the Bedouin's lyrical singing. The rababa strings are of thin wire and those of the sumsumiya are of horse-hair. The musicians hold a lowly position in the tribe and their work as singers and accompanists is regarded as an inability to perform manly labor. Most of the musicians are either elderly or disabled.

The Bedouin Woman

There is a concept whose roots lie deep in Bedouin society and which later on became an important part of Arab society as a whole. This is the concept of 'ard', normally translated to other languages as 'a woman's honor', but this translation is convenient rather than exact, for no other language possesses a term which exactly conveys the social significance of this concept. Actually, when a Bedouin or any Arab uses the term 'ard' he is referring mainly to a man rather than to a woman. The expression 'his ard' is much more often used than the expression 'her ard'. This is not semantic quibbling but something that goes much deeper and reflects the Bedouin's attitude to women. When a Bedouin speaks with pride of his unsullied 'ard' he means mainly two things:

1. That no man has ever dared to dishonor him by dishonoring his wife or daughter. This means that he and his forebears were powerful enough to deter any outsider from looting their property or raping their women.

2. That he owes no moral debt according to Bedouin tradition and carries no stain upon his honor which would force him to abandon and sacrifice all he has until it is removed.

This is clearly expressed in the Bedouin saying "An offense against your property is preferable to an offense against your children, and an offense against your children is preferable to an offense against your ard."

The Bedouins believe that it is possible to erase any mark of shame – 'ar' – that a man sustains, except a stain on his 'ard'. That remains forever. For instance, if a man is killed by another tribe, his family can remove the mark of shame from themselves by killing a member of that tribe in return. But if a woman's honor is violated, the shame remains forever and her family will carry it for the rest of their lives.

Therefore the Bedouin attitude to women is patently ambivalent. A woman is perceived as both an asset and a burden. In a society of former warriors where the provider is the man and poverty is widespread, the birth of a daughter is close to being a catastrophe. The custom of 'wad-al-bnat', or burial of daughters has already been mentioned. A woman who bears only daughters furnishes her husband with a good reason to take another wife and even to divorce her in disgrace. Even King Hussein of Jordan, taking advantage of his Bedouin ancestry, used this stratagem to banish one queen and replace her with one who would bear him sons. 'Abu-al-bnat' or father of daughters is a sobriquet loathed among Arabs, Bedouins in particular. Added to the Bedouin's distress at the birth of a daughter is his grave and constant anxiety about her 'honor' after she reaches puberty. He is constantly filled with apprehension, and haunted by the nightmare that his daughter may be dishonored. The anxiety of her father and the responsibility of her brothers do not end even when a girl marries, for a woman who commits adultery or who is dishonored brings dishonor not only on her husband but also on her father and brothers.

On the other hand a woman is a valuable asset. Women are cheap labor and must always be obedient and cordial. The Bedouins have a saying that there are three things one must never lend – a sword, a camel and a woman.

And why should a Bedouin lend anyone his woman? After all, it is the woman who bears the burden of home and family. Her daily routine is very full. She is the first to rise when day breaks, to gather twigs for a fire to warm the tent. By the time her husband and children wake, the bread has been freshly baked and the warm drinks prepared. The eldest daughter takes the flock out to graze. In the event that there are no daughters in the family, this task falls on the wife as well. Water, the most vital necessity of the desert, is also the woman's responsibility. She carries it in jugs from the well, which is often very far. After she has brought the water, the woman prepares dinner for her family, and after the family has been fed she must gather fire-wood, weave tent flies and rugs, play with her children, and prepare supper.

Such a woman is an ideal spouse, an asset to any 'masculine' society. The division of tasks is almost sacred. A man must not carry water or gather fire-wood, and a woman must on no account tie up a camel, or slaughter a fowl or a goat. What this means is that a woman may not even touch the symbol of Bedouin masculinity – the camel, and that she may not decide important economic questions such as slaughtering a chicken.

Because of the matter of 'ard', a Bedouin woman must cover her face with a light or heavy veil which falls from the eyes down to her chest. This veil makes her life more difficult and makes eating, drinking and smoking more bothersome. Moreover, the Bedouin woman must wear black clothing despite the scorching desert heat. Shabtai Levi conducted a little experiment under desert conditions of which he writes: "Black is a color that absorbs considerable heat and seems to be the least suitable to desert conditions. When the air temperature was 28 degrees I measured a temperature of 54 degrees under the black cloth. For an air temperature of 32 degrees, the temperature under the black cloth was 57 degrees. This represents an addition of 25 degrees to the heat load. And when air temperature was 36 degrees, the temperature under the black cloth rose to 66 degrees."

These astonishing findings attest to the terrible hardship a Bedouin woman must endure when under such conditions she must get her work done. It is a cruel custom born of an inflexible tradition. The reason behind it is the necessity to cover the woman's body completely lest its exposure lead to her being dishonored and her 'ard' violated. Even ardent supporters of this appalling custom find it necessary to suggest justifications for such cruelty and some researchers accept their excuses. The rationalization is that the Bedouin woman who leaves her encampment to get water or to look for a lost goat or camel moves in an environment empty of people... The black she wears makes her conspicuous in the desert landscape even from a great distance, and permits her to maintain contact with her encampment. Should something happen to her, should she be attacked by a man or an animal, or bitten by a snake, this makes it easier to find and help her.

There is a story about a Bedouin mother who became worried about her daughter who had taken the flock out to graze and failed to return home. The flock returned without the shepherdess... A search party was immediately sent out and they found the girl groping among the rocks in the darkness.

How did the search party find the girl in the darkness when she was wearing black? That is a riddle.

Such stories are of great educational value. Difficult conditions are bound to cause protest and rebelliousness; and a strict, tendentious education is therefore of great importance.

Then there is the story of Hamda, who went out with her flock one day wearing white. She strayed far from her tribe and fell off her camel, breaking her leg. She was unable to move and no one could hear her cries for help. And because she was wearing white, no one could see her from afar. The flock returned without her, and Hamda died in the desert of hunger and thirst.

This story is sad and instructive, though no one has ever known a Bedouin girl to take out her flock riding on a camel. But no matter. The main point is the moral. In a society that does not punish severely, tradition is best maintained through education. Though the veil is a hindrance to a woman when eating, drinking or smoking, she has been so well trained to wear it, that she finds it difficult to take it off, even in special circumstances. Shlomo Arad who joined a few 'medical tours', tells of Bedouin women brought to a clinic for an examination. Though they agreed to undress, they absolutely refused to remove their veils.

But it must be said to the credit of the Moslem religion and Bedouin society that they have never accepted the Judeo–Christian view of woman as a temptress leading the man astray. When a man makes advances towards a woman, harasses her or commits an indecent act, he is severely punished. A man must come no nearer to a woman than a distance of half a meter, or the distance from which it is possible to touch or kiss her hand. When a couple is caught making love, it is the man who will be considered guilty. In his "Aspects of Bedouin Judicial Practice in Southern Sinai," Avi Perevolotsky writes:

"A man cannot claim that the woman seduced him, since if a woman tries to take hold of a man it is his duty to cut off the piece of clothing that she is clutching and to bring it as evidence at the inquiry. Even then he must refute the woman's claim against him by an oath and the act of 'bish'a', or licking a heated iron three times. He then rinses his mouth with water and shows the witnesses his tongue. If there are blisters on his tongue, he is held guilty. If no blisters appear, he is innocent."

Obviously, after licking a red hot iron three times no tongue will remain unscalded, so that the man's guilt has actually been decided in advance.

In a society which puts such a premium on a woman's honor and so jealously supervises everything to do with relations between the sexes, very clear cut restrictions and customs have evolved to ensure that the laws of separation between the sexes are fully observed. However, in Bedouin society, as in any other human community, a man is only flesh and blood and is driven by lusts and feelings. And a woman, too, is only human. So that even Bedouin society, with all its restrictions, has not succeeded in totally suppressing the woman's feelings and making her obey the demands made on her by the customs of society in guarding the honor of the man.

The Bedouin is jealous of his wife and reacts violently if another man attempts to get close to her, in action or even in thought. A whole network of customs and laws exists to protect the family. Convention even forbids one man's mentioning the name of another man's wife.

However, laws are laws and people are people. There are cases, however few, when a man's attraction to a married woman leads to intimate relations between them. While a man may be attracted to another man's wife, he will at the same time remain very jealous of his own. Despite the danger this entails, there will always be Bedouins who refuse to learn from the experience of others. The snatches of conversation one might hear between a woman and a man she fell in love with after his visit with her husband may go like this: 'Just look at the kind of good-for-nothing I have to live with. If only you knew how much I'd rather be married to you.' He might answer: 'You annoy me with the way you talk.' And she'll respond with a wink.

Bedouin society is aware of the tensions created by such strictly prohibitive laws and customs and has evolved mechanisms to relieve these tensions and express the woman's hidden desires openly and in permissible ways. Two such relief mechanisms are the 'wataya' (stooping) and the women's dancing at the 'zoara' (pilgrimage to a saint's burial place) and at weddings.

Shabtai Levi describes that during the 'zoara', it is the custom for the young men to have a camel-riding competition. The criterion by which the riders are judged is not the speed but the elegance of the riding. The competitors gallop in a row along the track while the women sit watching them and show their admiration and encouragement of a particular rider by making clicking noises with their tongues. Afterwards, when the families prepare to return home and the men are mounted on their camels, a woman who admired a particular man's riding may openly go to him and present him with a gift of delicacies (sugar coated bread, salted hard-boiled eggs) wrapped in a colorful kerchief. She does this in front of her husband and all who are there to see. It is her privilege. She approaches the rider of her choice, pulls the tassels of his saddle and he, though he may not even know her, stoops to accept her gift. Hence the name of the custom – 'stooping'. When he returns home he prepares a return-gift (a ring or a string of beads) wrapped in a kerchief. If he doesn't know who his admirer is he asks among the women of the tribe, and when he discovers her identity he sends her his gift, with his sister or a child acting as messenger.

The second custom is that of a woman dancing before a row of dancing men. It is practiced at weddings and tribal 'zoara's. On such occasions the dancing lasts all night. One of the favorite dances is the 'dahiya', in which a row of men, standing close together, moves forward and backward in a particular dance-step while an anonymous young woman dances before them, to excite and inspire them. Though the men like to have a woman dancing before them and though without her their dancing would lose its relish, no man wants that woman to be his sister or his wife. If the woman is one of their family, as must happen at some time or other, the men pretend not to recognize her and continue dancing. The woman dancer wears a veil, and in the dark she is not so easily recognized by her eyes and forehead only. Nevertheless, the dancer's brother or her husband publicly scolds her for dancing and sends her away, and sometimes, when they get home, he may even beat her. One young man told us that he had been forced to seek refuge with another tribe after stabbing a young man who had not let his sister perform her dance.

Though Bedouin poetry surrounds the woman in a romantic aura, Bedouin law treats her as a minor not responsible for her actions. The emphasis is on deterring the man from any action that would dishonor her. In principle, young men are not allowed to be in the company of young women. Even if the young man has not dishonored the girl, or even touched her, the girl's family may bring charges against him for just being with her. By law, a young man found in the company of a girl may be beaten, or his property damaged, and he has no legal recourse.

Therefore it is the man who bears the responsibility to keep away from a woman and to ignore any opportunities she may offer, or even her explicit invitations. For instance, if a man uses the chance presented by a woman's shaking hands with him to caress her hand even lightly, his punishment is 40 camels; that is, the same punishment as that for rape.

The Bedouin stops treating a woman as a minor only when she is old; that is, when she has ceased being a sex-object. Only then does she have the right to sit with men, to speak to them directly and openly, and even to smoke in public. However, very few women achieve this honored status, since life expectancy in the desert is very short.

From the day she is born, a daughter is considered a 'hemel', or burden, by her father. The girl must accept this attitude but she becomes very close with her mother, who prepares her for her role – that of a good, obedient wife, always congenial to her husband, a good cook, able to run an exemplary household, and raise her children properly. Only when very young is a girl allowed to play in the company of boys. The mother is the first to know when her daughter starts menstruating. The father discovers it the following day, when he sees that she has begun wearing a light, black veil. From then on she is bound by all the restrictions imposed on women; she has become a sex-object. Men begin to show an interest in her and the process of matchmaking begins. The men who seek her hand in marriage must first find out if she has any cousins on her father's side of the family, since they have undeniable priority. The Bedouins say that a cousin has the right to remove his cousin even from her bridal procession, if he wants to marry her.

After marriage the woman exchanges her black veil for a red one, which serves as a 'hands-off' sign to all men. From the moment the bride moves in with her husband her testing-period begins. This is a period of anxiety for her, in which she must prove her fertility, since if she is barren her husband may divorce her without proper compensation. Since there is no medical examination, the husband is never assumed to be at fault. Even if a woman proves her fertility, her husband has the right to take three more wives, if he has the means to support them. The Moslem religion allows a man four wives. In practice, a wealthy man who is so inclined may divorce and marry as many wives as he pleases.

In such a situation, where the man is free and all-powerful and the woman's world is limited to her encampment – and even there she is hedged in by restrictions on all sides – the man must take steps to prevent the situation from exploding. He is high-handed with his women, keeps a very watchful eye on his wife and makes up stories whose morals prove the inferiority of women. One such story was told by Shabtai Levi:

It seems that some women were sitting together, telling each other their troubles and complaining of the injustice done them by men. Said one, "The men have their sheik, why shouldn't we women have a woman-sheik?" So they decided to send a delegation to the men and demand the appointment of a woman-sheik. But the men adamantly refused to listen. The women discussed the matter, seeking ways of dealing with their stubborn and defiant men. Finally they decided to strike. The following morning the men got up and found their wives asleep. No bread had been baked and no breakfast prepared. When the men asked their wives to get their breakfast, the wives said, "Get it yourself." When the sheep returned from pasture they were not milked. "Why aren't you milking the sheep?" asked the men. "Milk them yourselves" said the women. And so it went. The men were angry and didn't know what to do. "Why are you doing this?" they asked the women. "We want a woman-sheik," the women answered.

Seeing that they had no choice, the men agreed. A

woman-sheik was chosen and life returned to normal. The new sheik sat on the council of elders, expressed her opinions, and seemd no less wise than any of the men. Then the women considered what demands they would present to the council of elders and decided they would ask them to change the laws of marriage. When the council convened the woman-sheik spoke. "We women are being discriminated against," she said. The elders were angry and asked: "What more do you want of us?" The woman answered, "We want the right to marry more than one man, just as the men are allowed to marry more than one woman." Hearing this, the head sheik rose, ordered his servant to bring him a bowl, some milk, and some water, and to set them before the woman-sheik. "What is that for?" she asked. "You will see," replied the sheik. He then told the servant to pour the milk into the bowl, which he did. Then he told him to add the water to it. This he did. The sheik then addressed the woman: "Please separate the milk from the water." "That is impossible," she answered. "Then how will it be possible," said the sheik, "to distinguish the fathers of the children born to a woman who has more than one husband?" He commanded her to leave and not to return. Since that day there are no woman-sheiks.

Courtship And Love

Shabtai Levi heard this story from a Bedouin youth:

There was once a shepherd who lived with his family in the Faran Oasis and used to take his flocks to the high mountain tops, even as high as Mount Sarbel. His good wife and his sons always anxiously awaited his return from the mountains.

One day when he was sitting in the shade of a rock, resting, he saw two desert mice, a male and a female, frolicking; the female in front and the male behind her. It was obvious that he was courting her and that she was evading him. But the male persisted. Then, passing a bush, he broke off a little twig and placed it on the female's back. And suddenly, behold – a miracle! Abruptly the female turned around and began licking and nuzzling the male's head, as females do. The two cuddled a while, then turned and disappeared inside a crevice.

Observing this the shepherd thought to himself, "If this plant can inspire love in mice, might it not also do the same for humans?" So he plucked a twig from the bush and climbed down to the well, where he found some girls drawing water. Approaching the lovely Faruza, he stuck the twig in her shawl. He had hardly withdrawn his hand when she turned around, and on her face was a look of rapture such as a woman's face might take on at being reunited with a long-absent lover. She wiped her hands on her dress, left everything and began running towards him.

The poor shepherd, who had not expected such a sudden reaction, was taken aback and began running away. But Faruza ran after him, calling, "Wait for me, my love, don't leave me, my heart yearns for you so!" The other girls wondered at Faruza's behavior, for her modesty was as well known as her beauty, and clapping their hands called after her, "Faruza, Faruza come back! What is the matter with you? You, running after a man?" But Faruza stubbornly and persistently followed the shepherd and kept calling after him to wait for her and give her his love. The shepherd climbed a precipitous cliff but she climbed after him like a goat. During her climb the veil slipped from her face and her tear-stained face looked all the more beautiful. All this while, the girls were watching from below, and their wails intermingled with Faruza's entreaties. Embracing him, she begged him to give her his love. Suddenly the shepherd pulled the twig out of her shawl and threw it aside. Immediately there was a change in Faruza's behavior. She was struck dumb. Then, covering her face with her shawl she climbed down to the well, and walking back and forth kept crying and wailing. She was like one dazed and could not understand what had induced her to do such a shameful thing as loving a man. The other girls understood that they had witnessed a magic spell. They straightened her dress, covered her face with her veil, comforted her and pretended that nothing had happened. But when they returned to their tents they told their parents the story of the shepherd who had put Faruza under a spell using a twig of a bush. The parents, who apparently no longer felt any love for their spouses, became very excited and asked, "Where is that bush? Who is that man?" But the shepherd, seeing what shame he had brought on Faruza, loaded his belongings on a camel and took his family to live in another country.

The people looked for the bush but no one has yet found it. And since that day there has been no love in the desert.

This innocent story, full of contradictions, was cited in full because it is instructive and reflects the existing reality.

The statement that "Since that day there has been no love in the desert" is close to the truth. In this desert society there is no connection between love and marriage. Marriage is based exclusively on economic and social considerations, and love might even become a stumbling block where such 'serious' considerations are involved. Love is not just superfluous; it is forbidden. In order to 'do a shameful thing such as loving a man' a girl would have to be mad or bewitched. And so it cannot be said that the Sinai is an oasis of love. Love there is a forbidden fruit and takes place in secrecy, in hiding.

Young men are expressly forbidden to come near young girls. The separation between the sexes is rigid. However, human nature and human drives cannot be totally suppressed. The strictest taboos and the severest punishments cannot subdue the tempestuous passions of youth.

A young man may not come near a girl's tent. Since the tent is in an open area with no vegetation around, he could be discovered immediately if he tried. In the encampment there are no walls, no hiding places, and everything is seen and heard. The girl is constantly watched. Even when she goes off a distance from the encampment, she can be watched because her black dress makes her conspicuous against the tan desert background. Despite all this, young men and girls do enjoy some moments together. It is the girl's task to take the flock out to graze and to water at the well. She wanders after her flock to crevices and corners far from prying eyes. Men are allowed to go to the well to drink, and between sips they can steal a glance, whisper a word, be bold and pay a compliment, and fix a rendezvous. Acting in collusion, the girls cover for one another. A girl seeing someone on the sly will never be betrayed by another girl.

The young men endanger themselves to keep the rendezvous. Obviously they don't come to the tryst with a bouquet of flowers in their hands. For one thing, there are no flowers in the desert. They reach their hiding place, deep in some ravine, on foot or in a battered car. In Spain a love-sick suitor takes his guitar and sings a serenade beneath the balcony of his beloved. The modern Bedouin youth has recourse to a love-accessory of a different kind – he brings a tape recorder with cassettes of the best lyrical songs in Arabic. He needs it. The Bedouin youth is not well educated. His life is rigorous and coarse. He does not express himself freely and beautifully. His vocabulary is as meager as the desert vegetation. Therefore he relies on Farid-al-Atrash, Abd-al-Wahb, Oum Khoultoum and other singers to convey to his beloved the love burning inside him.

Such trysts do not always end well, with the lovers kissing and parting with fulfilled and radiant smiles on their faces. In Avi Perevolotsky's "Aspects of Bedouin

Judicial Practice in Southern Sinai" there are some examples of what happens when things go wrong.

"Selim, the son of Hamed Abu Hajazi, and a friend of his took his car and went out to flirt with some girls of the Mezaina tribe. The men of the Mezaina caught them, beat them, took their car and brought them to Tarfa-al-Kordin. A trial was held and Selim and his friend were fined I.L. 10,000. According to Bedouin law, a boy caught with a girl may be beaten, his property may be damaged and he has no legal recourse."

Neither do desert Don Juans fare very well. Consider this example: Saadi Abu Masoud is a young man of the Jabeliya tribe who was recently married. Despite his marriage he often wanders in the wadis of the area and flirts with the shepherd girls. Though he was repeatedly warned by Bedouins of the Awlad Said tribe in the Naphah Valley not to come near their girls, he was caught one day in the company of a young shepherdess. His claims that he was there only by chance were of no avail. The Saidis seized him, beat him and wreaked havoc on his property.

Rashid Rashidi is a lawyer and a relative of the Saidis. Turning the situation to advantage, he quickly sent off a message to Abu Masoud's family to the effect that if he met any of them he would kill them, as the law allowed. They took the hint and paid him a compensation of I.L. 2,000.

As we have seen, marriages in the desert are not made on the basis of sentiment but rather on a 'firmer foundation' such as economic interests or the desire to strengthen the ties between certain families. Therefore the forbidden alliances usually end in painful separation, with the girl married off to a man chosen by her family rather than to the man she loves. Her wishes are not considered.

The story of Eid is a case in point. Eid was seventeen years old and in love with Subhia, a shepherd girl of a family of his tribe. They had been lovers for some time and the people of the tribe knew that something was going on between them. Eid used to meet Subhia secretly, and they would have tea together and make love. She used to meet him even if she was in the company of other shepherd girls, since it is an unwritten law that no girl informs on another.

One day Shabtai Levi met Eid and saw that he was

looking sad and depressed. He asked him what was the matter. "Have you got a headache?" "No," answered Eid, "a heartache." It turned out that on that day Subhia was married to another man. The lovers had been torn apart.

It is not only through marriage that young lovers are separated. In the desert there is no permanence. The Bedouin wanders in search of pasture, in search of a livelihood, in a never-ending effort to ensure his survival. And as he wanders his family goes with him. A love that blossoms when the lovers are neighbors and can meet by finding ways to slip away from watchful eyes is always in danger of being broken off. The young man may wake up one morning to find that the tent of his beloved is gone. Scrutinizing the horizon, he will find no clue of her or her flock. Only a few lifeless objects are left behind to remind him of her existence. The routes along which the Bedouins wander have become trails of tears for romantic souls in the desert. From his earliest days the Bedouin has had to accept the rigorous terms of desert life; but there are some sensitive souls who can't resign themselves to these terms. For years they look back with yearning on their first love, which was nipped in the bud as if by sorcery. Such longing for the past occupies an important place in the folklore, poetry and mentality of the Bedouins. More than a thousand years ago a Bedouin poet of the Arabian Peninsula said,

"Let us stop a moment
To cry over the remains of the past."

Following is another tragic tale of parted lovers.

Many years ago Higia Springs was all fields and gardens that extended across the wadi, from one mountain to the other and people used to call the wadi 'the beautiful valley'. Today the wadi is desolate. A flood carried off everything and only a few palm trees remain.

In those days a boy who lived in Higia Springs fell in love with a graceful young shepherd girl who loved him too. They were very young and could not yet be married but they swore that when the time came they would be. No one knew of this love which blossomed in secret. The boy used to count the nights waiting for the day when he could send his father to ask the girl's parents for her hand. But one day the girl's family left for Wadi-al-Nil in North Africa, somewhere to the west. They packed up their belongings, loaded the camels and left 'Wadi Jamil', the beautiful wadi, taking the girl with them.

The boy's sorrow knew no bounds. Each day he was more brokenhearted. His longing for the girl was driving him to abstraction. He began frequenting the caravan routes to ask people if they had seen or heard of his beloved. He questioned every wayfarer.

The girl, too, suffered the pangs of love and longing. One day when she could bear her yearning no longer she headed for the caravan routes leading to the Sinai, which go past Wadi Jamil. She stopped a young man leading a camel and asked, "Can you take a heavy load and carry it to its destination?" "How much does it weigh?" the young man asked. "A quarter-weight of salt," she replied, hinting that she spoke of a light but valuable load. When the young man refused, she asked another, but he too refused. After asking several other young men, she met an old man who understood what she was feeling and agreed to carry the valuable but light load.

This load was nothing more than an unwritten love letter, a coded message which he was to remember word for word and give to the young man if he met him. And he did meet the love-sick young man, waiting among the caravans passing through his wadi. But the old man had forgotten the exact wording of the message and the young man therefore misunderstood it. He thought his beloved was asking him to kill the old man who carried the message. He killed him.

The fact that the Bedouins lack a simple means of communication such as mail can turn a separation into a final, tragic severance.

While teen-age love can be fraught with dangers and often ends in tragedy, there is another kind of love, which is so dangerous that most Bedouins prefer to ignore it and even deny its existence. That love is the love between two people who are both married, and it is a terrible thing in a society which has strict taboos on relations between the sexes and in which a man who takes advantage of a woman's handshake to caress her hand is considered to have committed a serious offense. In a society where the woman wears black and the man white and both move through life like chess-pieces on a chess-board exposed to many eyes, adultery is an impossibility.

Bertrand Russell paints an inconceivable picture of

the horrifying conditions in which prehistoric man could have committed adultery. He says that in the darkness of night the man would have had to crawl up to the woman lying next to her man and make love to her under the constant threat of being discovered and having his head bashed in with her husband's heavy club.

The Bedouin's sensibilities are probably more cultivated and refined than those of the cave-man. Temptation exists in the desert, and the stricter the taboo the greater the temptation.

When the cuckolded husband discovers the terrible secret he sometimes prefers to divorce his wife quietly under pretense of a quarrel rather than become the object of gossip and derision. However, where feelings are involved reason does not always prevail. According to Bedouin tradition only blood eradicates disgrace. Quite a few men have paid with their lives for their forbidden love. Perhaps it is for such a man that the woman in the following poem is crying.

"I climbed to the high mountaintops,
To the summit of Mount Mashduba,
To cry for my beloved who has been gone so long.
My tears flow in a stream.
The birds wheel and coast
Circling the summit of Mount Juba.
In God's name, I ask you, oh vulture,
Have you any good news for me?
And the broad-winged vulture answered:
I bear bad tidings to sadden your heart,
Your beloved is laid over with dust,
His clothes have been flung among the tombstones.
Said she: A knife has been plunged in my heart,
It has pierced and stabbed this oppressed body.
I beg you, God of love
Take what is left of my life, and give it to those who can enjoy it."

Divorce

Existence in the desert would be impossible without a firmly established and stable family life. Constant confrontation with rigorous conditions makes harmony within the tent a vital necessity. The woman's work is hard and her duties from dawn to dusk are manifold and exhausting. She takes care of the children, gathers firewood, draws water from the well, cooks, cleans, serves her husband and turns the tent into a home he can be proud to bring his guests to. In addition to the heavy burdens which this way of life places on the woman, it also imposes a complex web of taboos, restraints and suppression of desires. Moreover, the opinions of a girl are not considered in the choice of the husband she must serve obediently and with devotion, whose children she must raise lovingly, and whose flocks she must tend diligently. Besides all this, there is the ever-present threat that her husband may take a second or third wife, in which case she is cast off and excluded, and her husband's affection is bestowed on his new wife. The picture becomes even gloomier in the case of a teenage girl married to an old man, and there are cases of seventy or eighty year old men marrying twenty year old women.

This is a dangerous situation which holds the seeds of calamity within it and threatens the very existence of the family or, in other words, the Bedouin's very survival in the desert. A society which creates such a situation must evolve counter-measures in order to ensure that it functions well and survives. Paradoxically, Bedouin society has hit upon a very original solution to the problem, which might be dubbed 'stability through absence of stability'. The secret lies in the belief that what is important is not the emotional bond between husband and wife but the stability of the family. The solution is simple but surprising, given a society as bound by tradition as that of the Bedouin. The solution is the institution of divorce.

A survey conducted among seventy families in a certain region of the Sinai in 1978 showed that 17% of the women had been married more than once. According to some estimates the divorce rate among the Bedouins is as high as 30%. Such a high divorce rate is astonishing and almost unequalled in the western countries where permissiveness is rampant and where the institution of marriage is undergoing a process of disintegration. But while in western countries divorce leads to the destruction of the family unit, among the Bedouins it leads to stabilization of the family, since it makes it possible to reorganize the family cell on a more harmonious footing by means of a more felicitous match.

The man reserves the right to ask for a divorce while the woman has no such right. It is enough for the man to pronounce the words "I hereby divorce you" and his wish will be honored and the marriage ties broken. If the woman does not remarry, the man also reserves the right to change his mind and remarry his former wife. Such a second marriage will cost the man considerably less than his first marriage to the same woman. It is enough for him to take a lamb from his flock, and slaughter it in front of two witnesses. He can repeat the same tactic once more without significant cost. But after the third divorce, remarriage to the same woman becomes more complicated. The same problem confronts the man if he declares before his wife during his first divorce "I hereby divorce you thrice". In both cases another man must enter the picture before the husband can remarry his divorced wife; that is, the wife must first marry another man (even in a fictitious marriage), and be either divorced or widowed before she can again marry her former husband. This is the custom not only among the Bedouins but among all Muslim Arabs.

Despite all that has been written on the subject in romantic literature, the Bedouin values his property highly. That is why a man who has decided to divorce his wife is careful to announce his fateful decision outside the tent, for, should he lose his temper and make the announcement inside the tent, the tent and all that's in it will become the property of his wife, in place of the usual compensation he would have to pay her if he made his announcement outside the tent.

In contrast to a man's announcement of divorce, such an announcement by a woman has no legal significance. She has two choices:

1. To go to court and demand a divorce.

2. To make things so difficult for the man that the only choice he has is to announce his intention to divorce her.

A Bedouin will divorce his wife if he has either caught her in the act of making love to another man or seen another man, who had no reason for being there, leaving his tent while his wife was in it; if she neglects her duties as a housewife in cooking, cleaning, etc.; if she fails to take good care of the children; if she is deliberately wasteful; if she refuses to have sexual relations with him; or if she is barren. These are the main reasons, but any behavior on the part of woman which the man finds undesirable can be a ground for divorce.

A woman is entitled to a divorce without her husband's consent in the following cases: if her husband is impotent or sterile, if he cannot support her, if he will not have sexual relations with her or if he does not provide her with food, clothing and jewels. She must take her claim to her father, brother or another male relative and he will negotiate the divorce for her. The woman herself is not entitled to take her claim before her husband or before the judges.

There is also a custom which allows a woman to run away and seek refuge. Immediately or shortly after being married a woman sometimes runs away from her husband, seeking refuge in the tent of one of the tribe notables. A woman who has run from her husband and found refuge with a neighbor enjoys full protection. If her husband follows her into the neighbor's tent he is considered a trespasser. The person granting the refuge usually tries to mediate between husband and wife and if he succeeds he even appoints someone to guarantee the woman's safety when she returns to her husband.

Although the Bedouin bride is not consulted in the matter of her marriage, she has the right to leave her husband on her wedding night or soon after. In such a case the expenses of the courtship and the wedding are returned to the bridegroom and the marriage is annulled.

Perevolotsky in "Aspects of Bedouin Judicial Practice in Southern Sinai", cites an interesting case as an example and tells about the 'trial' that followed it.

There was a woman, daughter of one Moussa Atwa, who married one Oumdarwish. Six months after the marriage she ran away from her husband without taking anything with her and found refuge with a neighboring family of another tribe (the family of Rashed Rashidi of the Awlad Said tribe). Her father quickly came to take her back but she refused to go. Then the bridegroom came to Rashed Rashidi with his lawyer and his father-in-law to claim his bride. The bridegroom's lawyer claimed that she had kept house for her husband, cooked for him, tended his flocks and received his guests for six months. All this signified that she had consented to be his wife and had established herself as part of his household. If she had any reason to run away, he said, she should have done it right after the marriage and not six months later. After the intercession of the tribe notables it was finally decided that the bride's father would announce that he didn't want Oumdarwish as his son-in-law and Oumdarwish would agree to release the woman but with no property and his expenses for the bride and the wedding, I.L. 4,000, would be returned.

Afterwards a few interesting facts from behind the scene became clear. Before she was married, the woman had been in love with another man, Tha-Abu-Karsh. And sure enough, several months after the incident she was married to him as his second wife. Oumdarwish found consolation with his lawyer's niece, and some say that the money he got (I.L. 4,000) speeded their marriage. Between the families of the runaway bride and her forsaken husband there is still hostility over the insult to his family honor.

This goes to show that even in the desert, in a strict and rigid society there are some 'happy end' love stories. Between the lines we can also read that the runaway bride knew how to calculate her moves. She acted wisely and maneuvered her disappointed husband into a situation in which he could not harm her. But not all women are blessed with wisdom, certainly not girls who lose their heads for the love of another man. Sometimes, in desperation, a woman may abandon her husband and run away with her lover. Such a woman is vulnerable and completely unprotected legally. She may be killed and her killer is not liable to blood vengeance. The fate of her lover is even worse. He endangers not only himself but his entire tribe, since the family of the deceived husband has the right to kill four members of the lover's family, again without liability to blood vengeance. In addition, they may snatch as many camels as they can from the lover's family.

It is interesting how highly the Bedouin values his property and his live-stock. I know of no other society that has drawn up a 'price list' of material compensations for acts which bring dishonor on someone else or for moral offenses.

Avi Perevolotsky cites the following possibility:

"If the runaway couple finds refuge with a neutral family, the blood vengeance may be commuted to a fine. The husband's family will receive as compensation 20 camels for each day of the first week after the couple fled, that is, a total of 140 camels, plus 160 camels in exchange for the four men. In addition, they will get the camel or the horse used by the couple in their flight, the man's weapons and the sum that the deceived husband paid for his wife."

Such an economic arrangement explodes two myths about the Bedouins. One is that of the Bedouin as a hot-tempered character who loves a fight, a warrior who solves all his problems, particularly those that involve questions of honor with the sword or the gun. The other, a myth fostered by the Bedouin himself, is expressed in the saying that it is better to lose your property than to lose your children, and better to lose your children than to lose your honor. And when a Bedouin speaks of losing his honor he means being dishonored through his wife. Still, as we have seen, honor can be reinstated by a certain number of camels and by a certain amount of money.

The Bedouins of several hundred years ago would probably turn over in their graves if they knew how far the concept of 'ard' has deteriorated. In the old days an incident of a runaway couple would have been followed by a terrible chain of raids, killing and destruction. Even today, in the second half of the 20th century, in modern and wealthy Saudi Arabia the concept of 'ard' is taken very seriously. Many probably remember the case of the princess of the Saudi royal family who left her husband and ran off with her lover. The world was in an uproar and there was a lot of sympathy for the brave, romantic princess. Many intermediaries tried to intercede quietly on behalf of the couple but to no avail. In a crowded square of the capital city the young man's neck was bared, and when the executioner beheaded him the crowd cheered. The fate of the princess who had obeyed her heart was no less bitter. She, too, was executed. Not a caravan of camels, nor even a fleet of Cadillacs, could have saved them from death.

How is it, then, that Saudi society, so sensitive about its image in world public opinion, continues the punishment of execution for such an offense while the Bedouin society of Sinai, which is ignorant and unaware of the significance of public opinion, has replaced punishment by death with punishment by financial compensation? I believe the answer lies primarily in economics.

Saudi Arabia has amassed amazing wealth. Thanks to its oil, the Saudi coffers are overflowing. The Arabian Peninsula did not know such wealth even in the early glorious days of Islam, when the Arab Empire was at its peak and many lands, in abject submission to the Bedouin-Moslem conquerors, surrendered their treasures. In a country which buys a fleet of planes for millions of dollars, what compensation would a few paltry camels be?

In contrast, the picture in the Sinai looks entirely different. While the ordinary Bedouin in Saudi Arabia keeps getting richer, the Sinai Bedouin has remained entrenched in his poverty. For him a slight increase or decrease in income is very significant; it may mean the difference between eating his fill or going hungry. Therefore, it would not be cynical to say that in the Sinai morality has yielded to economics and that uncompromising fanaticism is a luxury of the rich. That is not to say that the Sinai Bedouin is any less moral than the Saudi Bedouin; it simply shows that the former is poor and the latter is rich.

Blood Vengeance

Blood vengeance is one of the two cardinal values of Bedouin tradition, the other being hospitality. Blood vengeance is a custom that grew out of the special nature of life in the desert. The desert is sparsely populated. A man living without the protection of solid walls, of either a house or a stockade, in a tent which can barely keep out the wind, is defenseless against group attacks of pillage and plunder. In a situation such as this he needs an effective means of deterring his enemies. Blood vengeance is such a mean. It is a kind of collective guarantee given by a particular group to all its members. When one member of the group is killed, a crime against the group as a whole has been committed. The potential murderer must know that in killing one individual, which may seem an easy matter, he is exposing himself to the terrible threat of group vengeance.

From early childhood the Bedouin learns two basic lessons:

1. A murderer is never forgiven. In the desert there is no statute of limitations. The concept of time does not mean the same to a Bedouin as it does in other life styles.

Vengeance can wait. There is plenty of patience and plenty of time. Even death does not bring forgiveness. If the murderer dies, another member of his group, though innocent, will pay for the crime.

2. A murder cannot be concealed. Despite the wilderness, despite the dark nooks and crevices, despite the secret spots hidden from prying eyes, the murderer may be sure that he will be discovered in the end. The relatives of the murdered man will conduct a rigorous investigation, working with infinite patience and perseverance, following up every clue, sniffing the spoors. They will check out every rumor. They will keep asking and investigating, adding one shred of information to another until the murderer is caught.

The following story which appears in "Aspects of Bedouin Judicial Practice in Southern Sinai" will serve to illustrate:

After the First World War large quantities of military equipment and arms were left in A-Tur. Two Bedouins, one from the Aligat tribe and the other from the Hawitat tribe, decided to loot the equipment. On their way back the Aligi killed his companion, probably because he wanted the loot all to himself. The body was found but the murderer disappeared without a trace.

The brother of the murdered man was powerless to do anything and was very frustrated. As time went on and his brother's death remained unavenged, he became an object of ridicule and scorn in his tribe. When the men were sitting around drinking tea, he would be served an upside-down glass, as a mark of scorn for one who has not avenged the death of a relative.

For seven long years the brother frequented all the gathering-places of Bedouins, watching and listening, in the hope of picking up some information, until at last he succeeded in locating the murderer. But his success soured when he discovered that the murderer was well known for his prowess and courage and that in his capacity as a guide of Russian pilgrims who went from A-Tur to the monastery he always carried a rifle.

One day the brother lay in ambush for the murderer in Wadi Isla, planning to shoot him. Suddenly the murderer raised his rifle and with one shot he shot down a vulture coasting high up in the sky. When the avenger saw this, he lost his nerve.

One night the murderer had a dream and in his dream a black crow was pecking at his head. When he awoke in the morning his head ached terribly, so he left his rifle in the camp and went to gather firewood. That was the moment the avenger had been waiting for. Pointing his rifle at the murderer, he asked if he recognized him. The murderer answered, "You have trapped me. I am finished." Then the avenger shot him dead, turned his body over, and stepped over it, as is the custom.

This story is tendentious, and though it is hard to explain how the dream of the murderer on the night before he was killed came to be known, that is not what matters. Rather, what matters is the moral of the story. Neither does this detract from the value of the story as an illustration of an ancient custom.

Ancient Bedouin tradition was explicit: blood for blood. If any individual family, or tribe does not uphold the tradition of blood vengeance, their life in the desert is no longer worth living. If they put off vengeance or try to evade it, this is taken as a sign of weakness and they become easy prey for anyone who covets their property or wives. And so, even if moved only by the instinct of survival, they must take revenge. Otherwise, they are doomed. And for generations the Bedouins have been upholding this tradition and doing what is required of them. Sometimes they exaggerated and did their duty with too much enthusiasm, to demonstrate their strength and deter potential enemies. Very often the traditional blood vengeance turned into ruthless vindictiveness which prompted even more ruthless retaliation.

Obviously, this custom, having become so firmly entrenched in Bedouin life, and the fanaticism that accompanied it, made life in the desert a hell. The prophet Mohammed preached against it and fought against it relentlessly. As the messenger of a new doctrine and a leader trying to unite different tribes into one homogenous nation, he wished to institute a body of law which would grant the Bedouins security and put a stop to the endless chain of blood wars among the tribes. But Mohammed's doctrine took root only in permanent settlements; among the Bedouin tribes the Moslem religion has had only superficial effects.

No outside law may substitute for the custom of

blood vengeance. If a murderer is caught by the authorities of a foreign rule and given any punishment short of execution, he is still not exempted from the punishment of the tribe. After serving his term in prison, he will be tried before a Bedouin court and he must pay for his crime as if he had not been punished at all.

Nevertheless, time has had a certain influence even in the desert. The social developments and changes which have taken place in the desert in the 20th century have left their mark even in this sensitive realm. As the Bedouin raids of pillage and plunder abated, an economic solution to the problem of blood vengeance became possible. The substitute that provides a release from blood vengeance is the 'daya' or ransom.

Over the past few generations wise men, well-versed in Bedouin tradition and law, have drawn up a sort of 'price list' for murder, manslaughter, rape, robbery, or any other offense.

Araf-al-Araf cites some examples from that 'price list' in his book "The Bedouin Tribes in the Beersheba District":

A severed hand – 40 camels
A severed foot – 20 camels
The loss of an eye – 30 camels
A broken tooth – 1 pound Sterling
A severed finger – 1 baby camel
A broken rib – 1 camel
A plucked out hair – 1 M'gidi (Ottoman coin)
The loss of hearing in one ear – 3 goats and 2 kids
A gunshot wound – 10 camels
A superficial injury – 1 camel
A facial injury – 2 camels
Manslaughter – 40 camels

Avi Perevolotsky notes that in 1979 the indemnity for manslaughter was 40 camels + I.L. 12,000 + 'aora'. 'Aora' means that the party guilty of manslaughter must supply a bride for one of the relatives of the deceased and she must remain married to him until she bears him a son, as indemnity for the loss of the deceased. After that she can be released from the marriage or stay, as she pleases.

The internal Bedouin judicial system has evolved and improved with time. Judges have emerged, and lawyers who are skilled in disentangling the complex web of problems which arise in the desert and famous for their mediation in quarrels which in former days would have ended in bloodbaths.

The fine of 40 camels is very heavy. It is beyond the means of a Bedouin with an average income. Even a reasonably well-off Bedouin would be financially ruined if he had to pay such a fine. On the other hand, the Bedouin who is awarded the indemnity would become a rich man. In other words, if such a severe financial punishment were really meted out, it would not accomplish its aim but instead would intensify despair and hatred. The importance of this fine lies in its deterrent power in the desert conditions. As Avi Perevolotsky writes:

"A punishment such as this serves as a strong deterrent to a poor Bedouin who toils the year round just so that his family can subsist and who usually has no savings and few possessions. The deterrent element is of great importance in Bedouin society, which has no police force or jails. The heavy fine thus serves as a red flag of warning to the potential offender.

Because the Bedouin is a wanderer, he finds it convenient to be able to leave some of his property behind unguarded. Herds of camels are left to graze freely far from the encampment, flocks of sheep are sent out to graze accompanied only by a young girl, the tent is left for hours unattended, emergency stores of food for a rainy day are hidden in the mountains and can be easily robbed, and where there are some plots where food is raised they are left unguarded. Such tempting breaches of security, coupled with the constant difficulties of survival in the desert, might lure a neighbor or passer-by, and it is the duty of Bedouin society to provide a strong deterrent to the would-be offender. Without such a deterrent it would be difficult to imagine Bedouin society, which functions without a police force to arrest and investigate suspects, without insurance companies to cover the damage, and even without shops where stolen or damaged items can immediately be replaced."

Thus the first principle of Bedouin justice is deterrent power; i.e., heavy fines. However, this principle in itself could not work indefinitely and might have led to the social and economic breakdown of Bedouin society. For this reason another element has been added, namely, the principle of "harame" or concession. After the severe punishment which leaves the accused in a state of shock, the process of 'harame' begins. The circumstances of the offense, the offender's past, his lineage and economic position, his suffering and his humiliation are all taken into account. The judge then brings psychological pressure to bear on the plaintiff, taking advantage of his high position in the tribe. He may not hesitate to address the plaintiff thus: "Out of the respect and admiration you bear me I ask you to concede somewhat as to the punishment of the offender." He may then bring social pressure to bear, saying: "For the sake of the honored witnesses and the esteemed spectators who followed this trial, it would be proper to concede a little more." The judge might not even disdain flattery, saying: "Surely a man as well-known for his generosity and compassion as yourself will not miss this opportunity of proving his virtues."

Sometimes the judge speaks to the plaintiff privately and they agree in advance on the extent of the concessions. Generally the plaintiff does not prove stubborn. He knows that one day the situation may be reversed and he may find himself on the defendant's bench in desperate need of someone else's compassion. That is why the concession generally amounts to a large part of the fine imposed. Sometimes the fine actually paid is a third of the fine imposed, and at other times, thanks to "harame", the defendant even escapes without any substantial fine.

The third principle on which Bedouin justice is founded is the discovery of the truth. In the desert the population is sparse and there are usually no witnesses to a crime. Moreover, in a society without a police force to conduct criminal investigations and without means of criminal identification, it is difficult to get the accused to confess. In this matter Bedouin justice relies on the ignorance of the Bedouin, his superstition, his hidden fears and his naivety. The Bedouins have a 'lie detector' of their own, parallel in function to the polygraph used by modern police – an oath on the grave of a Bedouin holy man. Bedouin society has such holy men, who are believed to have magic powers, even after death. Alive, they have the power to cure diseases, make barren women fertile, and promise sons to families blessed only with daughters. After his death, the powers of the holy man are believed to be transferred to his grave. One of these powers is the ability to tell whether a person is telling the truth. A Bedouin on trial would have to be immensely strong emotionally to deny the truth when faced with the magic powers of a holy man's grave.

In rare cases the accused may show strong resistance and pass the test without batting an eyelid. In such cases the prosecution will insist on employing the method of 'bish'a', literally translated as "the horrible". This requires the accused to lick a heated iron with his tongue. If he is telling the truth, he will come out unscalded but if he is lying his tongue will be burned. If he is lying, the accused generally breaks down before undergoing this test.

Perhaps this is the place to correct a few commonly held false notions about the Bedouins. In contrast to other Moslem societies, the system of justice among the nomads imposes no corporeal punishments. Islam subscribes to the principle of "an eye for an eye and a tooth for a tooth". To this day there are some Moslem countries which follow ancient Moslem law. When a thief is caught, for instance, his hand is cut off. But the Bedouin never took Islam literally. He took from the Moslem religion those precepts which were suitable to his way of life and paid lip service to the others. He exchanged the cruel corporeal punishments for fines as means of punishment and deterrence.

*"When a star rises in the sky,
you are no longer safe in the wadi.
You ought to pick your dates
even if it's night."*

The date is a symbol of the oasis. The Bedouin rests in its shade, eats its fruit and uses the fronds for a mat to sleep on and a basket in which to collect fruit. The palm tree is deeply embedded in Bedouin tradition so that severe punishments are imposed on anyone who damages the tree, regardless of its material worth. Nonetheless, it is interesting that a Bedouin wayfarer, tired and hungry from his journey, is entitled to eat as much as he can from the fruit of the palm. He may not, however, take any of the fruit with him.

"The desert is a treasure and the sea, sevenfold as much."

Bedouin fishermen handling their catch on the shores of the Red Sea.

The Bedouin's isolation in the desert
makes it necessary for him to provide for
most of his own needs. He gathers food
for his camel so that the animal will be
strong enough to plow the land; he
bakes his bread; and he prepares his
own clothing.

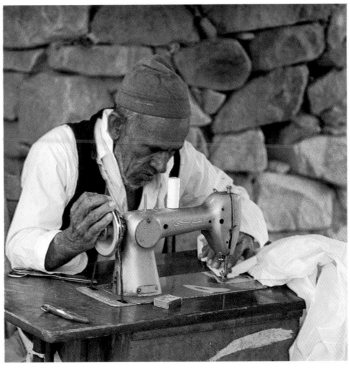

"Praise to Allah, the Lord of the Worlds,
the Compassionate, the Beloved,
King of the Day of Judgement.
You we worship
and You we seek for help.
Guide us in the Straight Path,
The Path of those You have favored,
Not the Path of those on whom anger
lies, nor of those who
are misguided."
Quran, Surah 1

Praying for peace: A Bedouin at the
Friday prayers next to an abandoned
cannon that remained in the area from
the Six Day War.
The Bedouin adapted Islam to his own
particular character and way of life.
Before praying he cleanses his hands
and feet with sand rather than precious
water and any piece of land may serve as
his mosque as he wanders from place to
place.

Most of the cemeteries in the desert were
founded near the grave-site of sheiks,
since burial alongside a sheik is a source
of honor and sanctity. The Bedouin does
not display his emotions in public and he
buries his dead in stoic silence. The
anonymity which is such an important
part of his life is part of his death as well.
He is buried with no sign or tombstone.
Even the stone that is put on the grave is
soon consumed by the sands.

An ancient caravan route crosses the Sinai Peninsula from one side to the other – from Abu Zneima on the Gulf of Suez to Dahab on the coast of the Eilat Gulf. The wayfarers of yesteryear chose to leave a record of their presence in the Muchtev (inscriptions) Valley. The cover that formed over the letters and paintings etched in the sandstone preserved these works for generations. Most of the inscriptions are in Nabatean script (derived from ancient Hebrew) and a few are in Greek letters.

Right: painting in the rock at Abu Jada. Graffiti by travellers and pilgrims of different historical periods are to be found along the caravan routes throughout the Sinai.

Ya'ar Ha-Amudim (Forest of Columns)
Left:
A rare geological formation resulting from a volcanic eruption. The columns are formed by lava substance and filled with lighter materials that were forced up through pressured gases produced by volcanic eruption.

Sarabit el Chadim
Right:
The history of Sarabit el Chadim dates back more than 5000 years. At the time of the first dynasty of Egyptian kings, the turquoise quarries and copper mines of Sinai were discovered in the area. The Egyptians built a temple in honor of Hathor, the goddess of Turquoise, for the overseers of the Semitic slaves who worked at the quarries. Hieroglyphic inscriptions are clearly seen carved on the pillars.

*"Three things broaden a man's mind:
running water,
green meadows
and a beautiful face."*

Left: A palm tree
In descending order:
1. The plant, common in the Sinai, is
thought by some botanists to fit the
Biblical description of Manna.
2. The Hyoscyamus is a source of toxic
substances which produce drowsiness,
sensory paralysis and low blood
pressure. The Bedouins use it for its
hallucinatory effects. There have been
known cases of death.
3. An Acacia tree.

The osprey (pandion haliaetus). In the Southern Sinai there is a large and quite stable hatching colony. The hatching period in the Southern Sinai is February-March. The osprey lives mainly on fish.

Opposite page
Above: Ibexes.
Center: The Sinai lizard (agamidae)
Below: The white stork (ciconia ciconia) migrates in large flocks in autumn and spring.

The court is in session

The basic tenet of Bedouin law is the imposition of heavy fines – a serious and effective deterrent. The worst punishment in Bedouin law is ostracism (tashmis) which uproots a Bedouin from the group responsible for his safety and well being – the family, the clan and the tribe.

The judge is a key figure in Bedouin society. Not only must he know the law; he must also be skillful at uncovering the truth.

The Bedouin women cover their faces from the eyes down with a long stretch of cloth that drapes to the chest, decorated with various coins and chains. This custom is the woman's sole demand, and derives from the need to "conceal her identity" which is a by-product of her isolation in the desert. By the same token, her suitor is also interested in guarding her from the eyes of strange men. At home, the Bedouin woman usually covers her face with a colorful cloth kerchief but whenever she goes out in public she wears the ornamented "Burkua" which is also a source of establishing one's status among the members of the tribe; for the more decorations a woman wears, the wealthier and more loved she must be. The Bedouin man is almost monklike in his simple attire. His sources of enjoyment are smoking, caring for his camel and sitting in his tent.

Mak'ad

A meeting in the Mak'ad

Mak'ad – a shaded shelter to be found mostly next to the sheik's grave. It is like a social club for men. Like most other Bedouin "institutions", the Mak'ad is geared to life in the desert. In it, one can find everything one needs for day-to-day survival: water, tea, coffee, sugar and cooking utensils. It is a most revered site from which no Bedouin will ever remove anything. In fact, the passerby is expected to leave something behind for the next user. There is a folk tale of a man who took a coffee pot from the Mak'ad. The pot stuck to his hand. It was not until he walked back to the Mak'ad after being told to do so by his god, that the pot was released from his hand.

Those who reach old age in the desert are venerated. Only in old age, when she ceases to be a sex object, is the Bedouin woman free to enjoy the company of men; to conduct open conversations with strangers and to smoke in public. The aged Bedouin woman assumes a quasi-holy character based upon a long life experience of survival in the desert. She becomes a fortune teller, a healer and an adviser.

Old men become closer to their sons who are often their source of support. The very fact that an old man may still marry a young woman gives the Bedouin a sense of rejuvenation even at an advanced age. Few men actually do start a new family in old age – mainly for economic reasons, especially when their other wives are still alive.

Hospitality

The following story appears in the first part of "A Collection of Proverbs", a book written by an Arab writer of the Middle Ages, Al-Midani:

"Once there was a very hot, dry year and all our livestock died. One night we were so hungry we couldn't fall asleep. My husband Hatem took Adia in his arms and I took Sufana and we played with them to get their minds off their hunger till they fell asleep. Then Hatem kept talking to me, trying to distract me so that I would fall asleep. Finally I took pity on him and stopped answering him so that he would think I was asleep and go to sleep himself. Several times he asked, "Mavia, are you asleep?" and when I didn't answer he stopped talking. Then he looked outside the tent and saw someone approaching. He sat up and heard a woman calling, "Abu Sufana, I have come to you and left my hungry children behind." Hatem answered her, "Bring your children here and as God is my witness, I will feed them."

I immediately got up and asked him, "How will you feed them, Hatem, in God's name? Your own children were so hungry they couldn't fall asleep until we distracted them."

In reply he got up and slaughtered his horse. He made a fire and urged the woman to roast some meat, saying, "Go on, eat, you and your children." Then he turned to me, "Wake up the children." I woke them and then he said, "It isn't right that you should eat while the others in the encampment go hungry." So he went up to each tent in the encampment, calling people to come to the fire. And they came and ate.

He himself sat looking on, covered in his blanket, till there was nothing left of the horse. He had not even tasted the meat."

Many generations of city Arabs and Bedouins were educated on this story of Hatem. To them he has been an example of generosity and hospitality. Many legends grew around the figure of this Bedouin benefactor and he has become a symbol and a source of pride. No one knows how much truth there is to the story. Al-Midani, who cited it in his book, lived several hundred years after Hatem is supposed to have died. But the legend survives and is known even among ignorant people who have never heard of Al-Midani and are incapable of reading his book.

Many writers with romantic tendencies, especially Arabs, would have us believe that hospitality is part of the Arab character because the Arab is an innately noble human being. This is not the place to take issue with that approach. Be that as it may, hospitality has become a hallowed social norm in the desert, just as it is among the Eskimos in the snowy wilderness. Still, there is a difference between the Eskimos and the Bedouins in their approach to hospitality. The Eskimo is apparently more jolly by nature than the Bedouin. He receives his guests with the sincere delight that a lonely person feels at the prospect of company. The Eskimo is as happy to have the guest stay with him as the guest is to be given warm shelter. The Eskimo offers his wife to his guest and calls their love-making 'sport'.

In contrast, the Bedouin takes hospitality much more seriously. To him it is a duty, a question of prestige and a source of pride. It is a supreme command imposed by the desert. According to Bedouin convention, hospitality is a privilege of the guest more than a pleasure for the host. In his "Aspects of Bedouin Judicial Practice in Southern Sinai" Avi Perevolotsky says that "there are those who claim that the guest even has the right to demand the hospitality due him before a judge and if he has not been treated properly by his host he has the right to proclaim in public "Such and such is a miser," though I have never heard of anyone availing himself of this right." At least not in the legal sense, that is. Socially, people certainly make use of this right. Quite a few guests malign their hosts, and the troublesome, sponging, contemptible guest occupies a place of honor in Arab folklore. Such a guest is viewed as a leech sucking the host's blood.

But the host must bear it. He must serve his guest, be

cordial to him and keep quiet. He may gnash his teeth in anger and frustration but he must obey convention. The law of the desert even permits the host something which is otherwise absolutely forbidden – to steal, if need be, enough to feed his guest. Such a theft is called 'adaya'. As Araf-al-Araf writes: "The Bedouins permit a theft committed by a host whose house is empty in order to offer his guest food. The 'adaya' is permitted where sheep are concerned and only for a guest who is already in the host's house but not for a guest who is expected. The owner of the flock must be notified that the animal has been taken, and taking one of his favorite animals is not allowed."

It is difficult not to wonder how a guest must feel when his host is obliged to swallow his pride and go out to steal in order to feed him. But such is the law of the desert. The positions could be reversed and the host might one day, when he is far from home, need his guest's hospitality. But it must be said that cases of a host stealing for his guest are the exception. Normally both host and guest show a sense of proportion and consideration without which the custom of hospitality could not survive. The Bedouins realize only too well that in a poverty-stricken society the principle of reciprocity is all-important. As you treat your friend today so will he treat you tomorrow. In other words, the same principle is at work here as in blood vengeance. The custom of hospitality is a consequence not of the Bedouin's magnanimity but of a need created by desert conditions. Desert journeys are long; until recently the only means of transportation were animals; the sun beats down mercilessly by day, and by night the cold is fierce; there are no roadside inns to serve man or beast. The Bedouin has been wandering for generations, and has alternately been both guest and host.

In the days when raids of pillage and plunder were an everyday event, the concept of hospitality included giving refuge. The smaller and weaker tribes were always prey to attacks of stronger tribes and lived in constant fear and insecurity. Some of these tribes would form alliances and unite in times of need to defend themselves against a strong enemy. Other small tribes would seek the protection of a large, strong tribe, sometimes for a certain payment. The early Bedouin poets, who used to praise the hospitality of their tribes lavished just as much praise on the tribe's ability and willingness to grant refuge to the defenseless and the weak.

The Camel

Just as in western civilization the car has, in the past few decades, become a symbol of masculine pride, so the camel is a symbol of the Bedouin's masculinity. This animal, which seems to many clumsy, stubborn and ugly, is perceived by the Bedouin as beautiful, graceful, gentle and faithful. The Bedouin man, even the warrior, differs from the Indian or African tribesman in his attitude to his body. The men of African and American Indian tribes take pride in their bodies. They adorn themselves with feathers, paint their skins, wear jewelry, take hours to beautify themselves, wear complicated hairdos, smear their bodies with colorful mud, point up the scars of their old wounds, and sometimes, as in the case of the Maasai, keep their wounds from scarring over in order to emphasize their courage. In contrast, the Bedouin is modest, at times even ascetic, where his body is concerned. He hides his body under a robe which comes down to his feet. He is not dandified, does not adorn himself and cultivates no outward bodily mark save his moustache. The Negro and Indian warriors seem like spectacular peacocks compared to the Bedouin warrior, who, like a wolf, is not impressive in appearance though he is no less ferocious and courageous than they are.

But all the adornment, ornamentation and luxury that the Bedouin man denies himself are bestowed on his camel. The saddle is of the finest leather. The camel is generously adorned with colorful beads and tassels and a beautiful harness. It is pampered and admired.

When a man returns home to his tent, his wife will rush to unsaddle his camel before she ministers to her hungry and thirsty husband's needs. When a stranger approaches the encampment, the right to be his host is reserved for whoever is first to remove the saddle from his camel.

The Arabic language contains dozens of terms of endearment for the camel. The name most commonly used is 'ship of the desert'. If the camel were at the height of its glory today, as it was in the past, it would probably be called 'spaceship of the desert', since from starting point to destination it is self-sufficient, requiring no outside supplies for its survival, save oxygen. The hump on its back serves as storage for the nourishment and fluids it needs in the hot parched desert. It serves the Bedouins in many ways and demands little in return. Its teeth, tongue and stomach enable it to eat even desert thorns. Its feet are wide and soft and will not sink even when the camel is heavily laden and is making its way in boggy sand.

The camel has provided the Bedouins with food that is invaluable in the desert – milk and meat. In times of hunger and when there is no pasture, the Bedouin slaughters some of his camels, especially the old ones, for food. He uses camel hair to weave cloth, and camel hide to make various necessary products.

The camel is the symbol of Bedouin masculinity and is flaunted at weddings, celebrations and pilgrimages. Camel-riding competitions are popular and very common. On such occasions the Bedouin appears on his camel in full splendor and even a severe and restrained society such as that of the Bedouin lets the bridle fall a bit and allows even married women to express their admiration for the best rider publicly.

In the Bedouin wars the camel used to be what the tank is today. Just as modern infantry are helpless against a tank, so the archers were helpless against the charging, trampling camel. Unlike modern wars, which are not fought for loot, the Bedouin wars were fought mainly for pillage and plunder, and the same camel which helped to gain the victory by serving as a tank during the charge, later served as a transport vehicle for all the loot taken from the defeated enemy.

But the importance of the camel goes beyond all that. The camel served as the economic foundation of Bedouin society. Until a few hundred years ago trade between Europe and the Middle East and between Africa and the Far East was conducted across the deserts. Ships used to carry the goods to the ports of the Mediterranean or the Red Sea and the Persian Gulf. Before the Suez Canal was dug, it was camels that served to connect between those seas. The camel, which the Bedouins raised and cherished, was sought after and vital to this active trade. Sometimes the Bedouins would accompany the caravans as guides and as guards against raids of other Bedouins.

The cars and trains of the 20th century have diminished the glory of the camel and done away with its role as the economic foundation of Bedouin existence. Even in poverty-stricken Sinai you meet more and more Bedouins riding in battered old cars. However, the Bedouin adapts to changes quickly and it is safe to assume that within a short time after the Israeli evacuation of Sinai the camel will again take its traditional place in Bedouin society. The lack of spare parts and the fact that he is cut off from sources of energy will return the Bedouin to his faithful ally, the camel.

But it is not the antiquated, dilapidated car of the Bedouin that has taken the place of his camel in trade. The camel has been replaced by huge transport cartels. The income which the Bedouin used to derive from the outside world by means of his camel has completely vanished. Today the Bedouin's contact with the outside world is in his capacity as guide, taking small groups of tourists to exotic places and allowing them to have themselves photographed on his camel, for a pittance. The Bedouin adorning many a tourist's album as he smiles stiffly for the camera, holding the reins of his camel, can no longer sing a song of praise to that camel. He will go on loving it, regarding it as a creature of beauty and grace, a symbol of power and masculinity, but he can no longer look upon it as a main source of income.

The tempo of the Bedouin's life, on the other hand, has remained basically similar to the camel's leisurely pace across the desert sands. It is true that during the Israeli occupation of the Sinai, when many Bedouins grew used to working at regular jobs, the time dimension became significant, but the tempo of life remained slow. Time is still a cheap commodity in the Bedouin's view of life.

In the expanse of the Southern Sinai you again and again come across groups of men sitting for hours round kettles of tea or coffee, engaged in conversation which to us seems idle. Yet the Bedouin looks upon this as almost his most important occupation. The Bedouin's perception of time is illustrated by the following story:

On his way to the Monastery of Saint Catherine through one of the less passable wadis, Shlomo Arad came across a Bedouin trying to repair an antiquated truck. When he asked the Bedouin if there was anything he could do for him, he asked for a cigarette and the two got to talking.

"Maybe there is something I can do to help you repair this vehicle?" Arad asked carefully.

"No," replied the Bedouin confidently, "with God's help, within a few days I will discover what's wrong with it."

"How long have you been stuck here?" asked Arad with great interest.

"Since the full moon."

According to Arad's calculation, that must have been at least three days. He thought to himself, "Such luxuries are reserved only for Bedouins." As if he had read his thoughts, the Bedouin said: "We Bedouins of the desert are blessed with lots of sand, lots of stars, and above all, lots of time." And it's true. Despite the fact that progress is slowly penetrating the Bedouin's way of life, his notion of time is very different from ours.

Poetry

The first mighty wave of Moslem conquest had two immediate aims: converting all the conquered peoples to Islam, and assimilating them into one nation. Both these aims were achieved almost in full in the vast space from Iraq to Andalusia. Only one people preserved its cultural distinctiveness and its language – the Persians. The Persians accepted the Moslem religion but resisted assimilation. Since then there has been a cultural war between the Arab peoples and the Persians. The disciples of the Arabic language and the Arab culture heaped scorn and ridicule on the 'backward' Persian language and extolled the Arabic language as pure, precise and beautiful. To these "fans" of Arabic, pre-Islamic Bedouin poetry was a paragon of artistic creation, to be guided by and emulated. The Persians did their share in this war of cultures. They regarded Arabic Bedouin poetry as backward art, poor in spirit, meager in content and primitive in form. In contrast, they held up the wondrous achievements of Sassanian culture, which flourished in the Persian Empire hundreds of years before the appearance of Bedouin poetry.

To this day, devotees of Arab culture view ancient Bedouin poetry as a masterpiece, and it is still taught in all Arab countries, from elementary schools to universities, as if it were modern poetry written by living poets. For a thousand years every Arab poet and writer who was worthy of the name had to memorize the poems preserved from the pre-Islamic period in the Arabian Peninsula, to understand their background and their meaning and to analyze their grammatical structure.

In the old days, every tribe of any importance had its own poet and the poet became a central figure in the life of the tribe. He was a combination historian, who recorded the annals of the tribe, minister of education, who assembled and cultivated a group of intellectuals, and bureau of psychological warfare, charged with glorifying the power of his tribe, raising the morale of the warriors and striking fear into the hearts of other tribes.

Al-Hajaz, a philosopher-writer who lived in the city of Al-Basra in the early days of Islam, said that the Bedouin tribal poet provided the Bedouins with the poetry they needed – he recorded and praised their victories, he uplifted their spirit, he exaggerated their power and he frightened their enemies. The poet of the rival tribe followed his words closely, and he himself followed with interest the writings of poets of rival tribes. Perhaps a poem by Al-Samuel, a Bedouin pre-Islamic poet, will illustrate the mission of the poet in those days:

> *"We are ridiculed for being few.*
> *My answer is that the noble are few.*
> *We don't mind being few as long as*
> *Those who seek our protection are protected*
> *While those who seek protection elsewhere are*
> *humiliated.*
> *Our days on earth are short, for we love death.*
> *Others hate death and grow old.*
> *No man amongst us has died a natural death*
> *And not one of our dead has gone unavenged.*
> *Our campfires have never ceased glowing for guests*
> *And those who enjoyed our hospitality have never*
> *condemned us.*
> *Our swords in the east and in the west*
> *Are notched from hitting armor."*

In the Sinai almost nothing remains of Bedouin poetry, which is still a source of pride to Arabs. The remoteness from the cultural centers, the isolation, the life of abject poverty, have turned the Bedouins of the Sinai into ignorant people, lacking even minimal education. Very few of them are literate. Poetry has been most severely affected by this cultural decline, though the Bedouin still needs poetry to express his longings, to enrich his celebrations, to convey his experiences to others and to pass on the heritage of the past. This need exists today as it did in the days of glory of Bedouin poetry, fourteen hundred years ago. And there must be talented people among the Bedouins today who could create richer poetry if they had the proper training. The image of the poet of the old days as spiritual leader and shaper of public opinion has lost its glory and is no more. Nevertheless, the Bedouin of Sinai has his poetry. It is poor like him and not very expressive, as befits his educational level, but still it is poetry to him. The poets of the Sinai are anonymous. No one remembers their names, no one honors their memory, but their poems are recited and their songs sung whenever the opportunity arises.

Mostly the songs are sung by the musician who plays the 'rababe' a violin-like instrument with one string. His music may be called the "music of celebrations", since it is at celebrations such as weddings and other happy occasions that the Bedouin listens to it. The singer-musician is a somewhat wretched figure and his status in the tribe is very low. He is usually very poor and often a cripple. And it is this sad figure who brings joy to others, inspires them and uplifts their spirit. He is not mocked like a circus clown, but he is a tragic figure, as befits the sad songs he sings.

> "Because I have no coins in my pocket, the beautiful eye
> has not noticed me.
> How can I enjoy being among people
> And how can I rejoice when I am so poor?
> I turned to the medicine-man and asked:
> Is there a cure for my pain?
> And he said: Your heart has been captured,
> How can I cure the distress of the soul?
> She who has captured your heart is pure
> She does not belong in this place.
> Her thighs are like the thighs of an ostrich
> And her hair is flowing and black.
> She is like a gazelle
> In a storm-seized land.
> I wish I had never laid eyes on her
> For I am powerless to win her.
> When I turn to her, others will be there before me
> And I, defeated, can only moan."

The helplessness of one who dreams of forbidden happiness and is powerless to make his wish come true is the central motif in the poetry of the Sinai Bedouin. He never blames the stars, and it does not occur to him to express bitterness or hatred towards others. He blames only himself. That is his fate and for generations the Bedouin has learned to accept his fate.

Acknowledgements

I wish to thank all those who were instrumental in my gaining an understanding of the desert and of its people.

My special thanks to Avi Rubens and Avi Ophir, of the civil administration in Southern Sinai, who gave of their time and energy to introduce me to Southern Sinai.

Thanks are due also to Moshe Sela, Yigal Karni, Danny Oren, Lika and Uzi Harari, all of the civil administration, who offered valuable help;

to Shimon Feinstein, Zeev Krupnik, Tsur Zoarts, Dudu Cohen, and Dudu Hamami, all of the Nature Reserves Authority in Southern Sinai, who made it possible for me to reach protected sites in Southern Sinai;

to the staff of the Cliffs of David Field School in the Saint Catherine's region, and particularly to Avi Perevolotsky;

to my Bedouin friends Hader and Mahmoud of the Gebeliya Tribe, and to Silmi and Suleiman of the Aligat Tribe;

to Barkat from Sarbit, all who opened their homes and their hearts to me, with much warmth and tolerance;

to Massada for publishing the book, and especially to Arye Ben-David and Doreet Scharfstein, for putting up with all my whims;

and finally, to my wife, Geulie, without whose help this book would not have been published.

Design: Arye Ben-David and Doreet Scharfstein

Translation: Shoshana Rothschild

Catalogue No. 00-3629